Best Wishes

To John

Pardner Money Stories

Deanne Heron

Deanne H   14/4/13

HANSIB

Published by Hansib Publications in 2011
London & Hertfordshire

Hansib Publications Limited
PO Box 226, Hertford, Hertfordshire, SG14 3WY, UK

Email: info@hansib-books.com
Website: www.hansib-books.com

A catalogue record for this book is
available from the British Library

ISBN: 978-1-906190-40-8

Printed and bound in the United Kingdom

DEDICATION

To my daughters, Sahara and Rebecca, my grandson Ishmail and to all my extended family from whom I draw my inspiration. To the colourful characters that make up all extended families

CONTENTS

ACKNOWLEDGEMENTS

Errol Williamson for being instrumental in getting my first short story published by the Jamaican Sunday Observer.

Alicia and Angela Henry for your help and encouragement.

Mrs Joyce Reader (deceased) for inspiring the poem which led to the stories.

"Mrs Areta Drew for being a true and supportive friend. The stories would not have reached the Jamaica Observer or Hansib Publications without you."

INTRODUCTION

Pardner Money Stories is a collection of short stories which takes a whimsical look at life within an extended black Jamaican family in Britain. It is written in English with Jamaican patois dialogue which captures the unique sense of humour of black people in situations which wouldn't ordinarily be considered humorous. It tackles subjects from funerals to family holidays looking at the interactions of various generations and highlighting the strong bonds of love and respect that cements them together and gets them through various crisis.

It was the death of 'the pardner lady' that really got me thinking about my rich culture which like many others in Britain, is disappearing as we are slowly amalgamated into a boring 'sameness'. Like many black people I was unaware of the value of my history and so full of the cares of every-day life, that I had no time to note and mourn the trickling away of my unique heritage. The death of the pardner lady inspired the poem which was the precursor to the stories. I didn't even know her full name – Mrs Reader (Joyce) I later found out but for decades she was just 'the pardner lady'; she who held sway over our finances for a small tip, with a rod of iron. The pardner, that well known savings club represented a culture; an eclectic mix of Jamaican and British from the fifties onwards, which has all but died but is worth preserving.

To me Jamaican patois is the most beautiful and expressive language ever developed. It is funny, vibrant, expressive and emotional. It's more than just words; it's body language, subtle nuance and intonation. It's a language of the soul, often more about what isn't said than what is – a look, a raised eyebrow, quick pout of the mouth or kissing of the teeth. Kissing of the teeth is a whole language in itself, conveying humour or anger to different degrees. I love the way one single word can be used to say several different things depending on the intonation and body language which accompanies it.

This brings me back to the pardner, sometimes referred to as 'the thing'. When I was growing up Jamaican people rarely referred to money by name. It was always 'de t'ing'. 'De ting' or 'de somet'ing' could actually be anything they didn't want to mention by name in front of anyone else and it was just accepted by everyone. A nod of the head, a pout and a grunt indicated understanding.

MY GOOD OLD DAYS

I'm feeling reflective today 'cos last year my neighbour died.
The big 'C' was whispered and I was shocked and sad but I never
cried.
She wasn't just a neighbour and she wasn't just a friend,
She represented something of my culture that had suddenly come
to an end.

She ran a pardner or paadna that exclusive black saving club,
That was our local when we weren't welcome in the oh so English
pub.
Brought from the West Indies, I don't know if the pardner is just
a Jamaican thing
That we've ignorantly thrown out and replaced with soulless
western bling.

Thrown out with our 'untouchables' Elloit Ness suits, gloves, hats
and brown grips,
Networking on the boat or plane for useful contacts or to pick up
survival tips.
The pardner was as much a part of us as ska, Milly Small and blue
beat,
And the brown paper we put in our shoes to keep chilblains off
our feet.

Do you remember the clubs, house parties, shabeens and red
stripe beer?

The things that took our minds off hard life, racism and the
constant fear.
The days when 'bad' didn't mean good and guns were children's
toys,
Not the weapon of choice for drug crazed teenage boys.

Tucked between our summer clothes were bottles of Wray and
Nephew rum,
Hidden at the bottom of the suitcase from the eyes of Her
Majesty's customs.
Mum said, a little for everyone and some to soak the dried fruit
for the cake,
Which at Christmas and Easter all the women would compete to
bake.

Oh Christmas… remember Cherry B, Baby Cham and the
Blauspot radiogram,
The tasteless turkey, washed down with advacaat, and spicy
curried lamb.
Christmas dinner was eaten with the best cutlery and china kept
in the glass cabinet,
And every year we all met at Alex Park carnival and prayed it
wouldn't be wet.

The 'pardner money'… how many times do you remember
hearing that phrase?
And how many young people know about pardner these days?
How that precious money was paid every week and you'd better
not be late,
With someone's relative back home waiting to put food on their
children's plates.

The pardner bought land, paid school fees and built or bought a
house,

The poor black man was able to buy a ring and make his girlfriend
his spouse.
Remember when winter was really winter, the fog, snow and
black ice,
The fun of coach trips, the men playing cricket, dominoes and
tossing the dice.

Then there was church whether Saturday or Sunday we didn't
have a choice.
What we did have then was a conscience, that still but not so
small voice,
Of your mother with her shopping trolley or maybe it was your
wife,
Who with 'the look' kept you on the straight and narrow, in fear
of your life.

The pardner was deposit and rent for that room you were the
wrong colour to get,
It saved your hide when you lost the money under the mattress on
that sure fire bet.
The pardner, another part of black culture is dead and buried,
from a bygone age,
It took its final curtain call, bowed to grateful applause and left
centre stage.

AUNTY DAR'S FUNERAL

We've been unfortunate recently to have a couple of deaths in our family. Funerals are usually sad solemn affairs. For my family and I strongly suspect many other Caribbean families, funerals are sad but never solemn when three, four or in our case five generations get together. Then all the family skeletons come out of the cupboard and I am given a sharp reminder of why I avoid certain family members.

Recently my aunt in London died. She was eighty-seven and had lived an interesting and full life so it was more a time of reflection and celebration of her life rather than mourning. She had a dry sense of humour and I imagined her looking down at us and having a good old chuckle.

All the men went to London separately in a van they borrowed, but that is another story altogether. They all know now that they will be suffering the fall out for many years to come. Halfway up the M1, I began to wish I had had the sense to go with them.

I made the mistake of deciding to hire a people carrier because the women couldn't all fit into my car. Although my cousin Barbara, Babsie to us, has been driving for over twenty years, she refuses to drive outside of Manchester or on the motorway. My mother gave up driving many years ago but has an advance licence for back seat driving which she uses to full advantage every time she gets into a car with me. The hire car was a beautiful, automatic, black Chrysler Grand Voyager, which looked the part except that I soon found out that it had VERY sensitive brakes. I really should have got the clue from the way I lurched out of Enterprise Rent a Car like a brand new learner driver. I slowly made my way home as if the car was having an epileptic fit with a line of traffic behind me beeping their horns.

My plan had been to leave Manchester at about 11.00am but at 2.15pm we were just getting onto the Princess Parkway.

I eventually got the hang of the brakes after I had almost launched the female members of my entire family through the windscreen a couple of times. Mum still won't believe it wasn't on purpose. I heard my cousin Myra or My as we call her, mutter, "Bwoy dem brake ya good een?"

"Yes, Missis," my mother answered. "Put on your seat belt good you hear, or you might reach London before the car."

They all thought that was really funny and mum chuckled mischievously, as she looked at me in the rear view mirror, ready for an argument. Cousin My patted my leg and shook her head so I apologised to everyone and didn't take the bait.

Cousin My and her teenage daughter, Tiana, who we call Tootsie, started to argue instead. Aunty Bliss, whose real name is Beverley, had to step in and tell Tootsie off for being cheeky.

"Bwoy, pickney these days feisty like chink," she said.

My teenage daughter, Laura or Lolly, made the mistake of asking what a chink was. My mum, Cousin My, Aunty Bliss, and Cousin Babsie then had a heated debate about the different meanings of the word chink and which one Aunty Bliss meant.

Aunty Bliss told Cousin My off for saying it was a person of oriental extraction although My didn't use those words exactly. Aunty Bliss folded her arms crossly under her ample bosom. "I am not going to sit in this car for one more minute and listen to a member of my family being racist!" she shouted. It's really funny how Aunty Bliss speaks patois if she is laughing or joking but perfect English if she is cross or being serious.

"So wha'apen, yu a goh jump out a de car at 70 miles an hour?" Cousin My asked. There was a moment's silence. I held my breath as I glanced at Aunty Bliss in the rear view mirror but she burst into thigh slapping laughter. Everyone else joined in laughing at the top of their voices. This went on for a good five minutes until they were out of breath and had tears running down their faces.

When they had calmed down, Cousin My said she wasn't being racist because everyone knew that Grandpa Charlie was half Chinese. Tootsie said she thought chink meant a crack. Lolly said she thought it was light coming through a crack. Everybody had an opinion. I kept quiet. After half an hour, I was very tempted to stop the car and put them all out onto the hard shoulder of the M6. Finally, they all agreed that it was an old expression from the days when beds were infested with lice and the chink Aunty Bliss meant was actually a bed louse.

For an overnight stay, my mum brought a large holdall, so stuffed that we could hardly get it to zip up. She had a shopping trolley on wheels, equally stuffed and four carrier bags containing enough food to "feed the five thousand on Jesus' day off", Aunty Bliss said. In complete contrast to her grandmother, my teenager's overnight bag contained her make-up bag, CDs, phone charger and no spare underwear or toothbrush. As she is a size 8 and let us just say I am not, blessed be the name of the 24 hour Tesco just off the North Circular East.

My sincere apologies to the man at the toll station on the M6 to whom my mother offered the plate of fried fish and plantain which she told him I had cooked. She said he looked as if he needed a good woman to take care of him and that I would get used to his bald head in time, fortunately not loud enough for him to hear. I put my £4.00 into the basket and drove off quickly because I knew what was coming. My mother bent my ears for the next ten miles telling me why she thought I was still not married. She added that she hoped one bad experience hadn't put me off men and asked if I was trying to tell her something by cutting my hair short and wearing trousers.

They then all had a discussion on what was wrong with men today. Aunty Bliss said Uncle Al, her husband, was the closest she had ever come to a perfect man. Cousin My whispered to me that he should be perfect by now as she had been remaking him for the past thirty years. We nearly had a fit laughing but we couldn't share the joke with anyone.

Cousin Babsie said I drove like a man. I wasn't sure if that was a compliment or not but I didn't want to set my mum off down that road again so I didn't ask. Later I overheard Cousin Babsie telling her husband, Ferdie, that I was a better driver than he was. She added that she would drive to the moon and back with me because I knew how to 'burn tyre' on the motorway.

"Pssstt," Ferdie whispered to me with a chuckle, "I will pay for the petrol if yu promised to take har to the moon and leave har there."

Cousin Petal, Aunt Dar's only daughter, asked me to say something at the church on behalf of all the family from Manchester. Cousin My took offence because Cousin Petal said I was the only one she could trust not to tell any jokes or say anything to offend someone from the platform.

I asked Uncle Al if his name was short for Alan because I'd only known him as 'Al' all my life. He cleared his throat and didn't answer.

"How much is it worth to keep your secret, Babes?" Aunty Bliss asked, putting her arms around him with a mischievous smile.

"Go away from me, woman," Uncle Al answered, "I've already spent a king's ransom over the last thirty years keeping you in shoes and handbags."

"Wasn't it you that told Papa when he said you could marry me that you were going to keep me in the style I was accustomed to?" Aunty Bliss demanded.

"Yu have to put me name down, Kelly?" Uncle Al asked, ignoring her.

"Yes, Uncle. Everyone's name has to go on. What's the big deal?" I asked.

Aunty Bliss looked at him with narrowed eyes, "The big deal is his name is Aloysius," she said.

"Lord, Bliss, how yu can do me so, man?" Uncle Al said kissing his teeth and turning his back to us.

"Ala ... who?" Cousin Babsie asked laughing.

"And you can shut up," Uncle Al said, "before a tell everybody yu no name Barbara, yu name Barbarian!"

"What?" we all asked, laughing.

"Shut yu mout, Al! A lie yu a tell," Cousin Babsie answered.

I found out later that it was true. Apparently, somehow at the registry office in Jamaica, 'Barbarian' had been written on Cousin Babsie's birth certificate and no-one had noticed for years.

Well, at least this time we all went to the right funeral. When Aunt Gwenda died at the beginning of the year, there was another funeral party at Southern Cemetery at the same time; Miss Pansy, an old family friend who came from our district in Jamaica. Half of us ended up at her funeral and half of her family at ours. It was the same when we got to the West Indian Community Centre. I thought it was a bit strange when I saw Cousin Babsie's car parked next door at the Catholic Community Centre. Then I saw Uncle Al and his sidekick, Ferdie, climbing through a hole in the fence looking sheepish with huge chicken drumsticks in their hands. When they saw me, Uncle Al put his finger to their lips and told me to shush. Later in the West Indian centre, I kept seeing people I didn't know tucking into curry goat and rice. I didn't understand at the time why the woman with the bad hair weave came up to me and said how sorry she was to hear about Sister Pansy and how they would miss her rum cake.

After Aunty Dar's funeral, when everyone had eaten their fill of fried fish, curry goat, chicken, several vegetarian dishes not to mention a ton of salad and coleslaw and drunk enough ginger beer to refloat the Titanic, we all helped to clean up the hall. Aunty Dar had been a strict Seventh Day Adventist Christian for most of her life and neither drank nor smoked. There wasn't a single drop of alcohol in sight and I didn't see one person smoking the entire day.

It took us about an hour to say good-bye. The men in their van must have been half way down the M1 before the women finished. We all started hugging and kissing at one end of the hall but by the time we got to the other end, people had moved and we couldn't remember who we had hugged already. Some of the kids thought it was great fun to be hugged and kissed and then run to the end of the line to be hugged and kissed again. It wasn't until we were half way home that we realised that no-one knew the little old man with no teeth who must have kissed everyone at least half a dozen times. Cousin Babsie swore that when he hugged her he pinched her bottom.

Aunty Bliss started crying and set everyone else off because she said it was a pity we only all got together at weddings and funerals. Marcus, one of the London cousins, made a bad joke about whether it would be a wedding or a funeral we would all get together for next time and whose turn it would be. Cousin Ailsa who is eighty-four hit him on his shin with her walking stick and told him not to look at her because she had every intention of getting her telegram from the Queen.

Oh, and by the way, Aunty Dar's funeral was lovely. Everyone scrubbed up well and looked respectable in black. The flowers were beautiful, the food was delicious and no-one fell out. Even though we all cried so loud we frightened the grave diggers as we put the flowers on her grave, Mum said Aunty Dar would have loved it.

WHEN FERDIE'S DRAGON STOPPED
WALKING THE TRAIL

I don't know how long I'd been asleep, but it felt like I'd only just closed my eyes when something woke me. I lay in bed listening intently and blinking in the darkness, thankful for the warm solid shape of Michael asleep next to me, his soft snores gently reassuring. I glanced at the clock which said 23.50. After a few minutes of not hearing anything unusual, I snuggled up to Michael and was just falling asleep when there was a loud bang in the front garden followed by a string of expletives.

Michael's snores stopped abruptly.

"What was that?" he asked in a loud whisper.

"Baby, I'm in here with you," I whispered back. "If I could tell you what that was, I'd have a job earning a fortune."

He quickly got out of bed and tiptoeing to the window peeped through a crack in the curtains.

"Can you see anything?"

"No." He tiptoed back to the bed, stubbing his toe on the side of the chest of drawers and swearing before sitting down heavily. Michael jumped up again immediately as we heard another bang.

"Ratid, somebody is trying to break in!"

The pain of his injured toe forgotten, he rushed to the door. I grabbed the window pole and followed him. He stopped suddenly on the landing, bending down to pick up one of his trainers. I slammed into him, almost somersaulting over his back. He turned his head, gave me and the window pole a curious look and shook his head.

"Where yu going with that? Yu crazy?" he hissed.

I hid the wooden pole with its small hook behind my back and smiled sheepishly. Then I looked at Michael's size eleven trainer in his hand.

"Well if you think you're going to scare a burglar with that, one of us is crazy!" I hissed back.

Michael continued down the stairs, trainer raised above his head, looking more menacing, bless him, in his boxer shorts than I'm sure he felt inside. Halfway down the stairs he looked back at me with a look which said, "I'm too young to die. Please let's just go back upstairs and call the police." His pride wouldn't let him say the words and I wasn't about to let my knight in shining boxers off that lightly.

"Go on, Babes," I whispered encouragingly. "If anyone thinks they're going to break into this house, we'll let them have it."

"You're not letting anybody have anything. Just stay behind me."

I gasped as I saw a huge shadow walk past the front door and nearly jumped onto Michael's back, almost knocking him out with the window pole. Michael suddenly straightened up with a snort.

"I'd recognise that bloody hat anywhere." He rushed down the last few stairs and throw the front door open.

"Uncle Al!" I cried. "What are you doing? You scared us half to death!"

"Scared you," Michael said. "Wha'appen to yu Al, man? Why yu creeping round people house dis time a night?"

Taking the window pole out of my hand, Michael turned and stomped back up the stairs to bed. Wishing I could go with him, my eyes followed the well shaped boxer clad bottom as it disappeared up the stairs.

I turned to see my uncle gesturing frantically to someone in his car. Ferdie, his best friend who is married to my cousin Barbara, known as Babsie, quickly jumped out of the car. Pulling his cap down over his face and his collar up, he briskly walked into the house with his head down.

"Evening, Kelly," he said as he walked straight into the living room. I stood speechless, holding the open door.

"Shut the door Kelly, man, before that nosy woman 'cross the road see us," Uncle Al said. "Ferdie need to talk to yu, you being a counsellor and all, and him don't want Babsie to know."

"I can only talk to him, Uncle."

"Yeah man, whatever. Wha'appen to Mixer why him in a bad mood?"

"It could have something to do with the fact that you just got us out of bed Uncle Al," I said. "We thought you were a burglar."

"Me! Mi never burgle nothing in mi life."

Michael, better known as Mixer, has been playing the music at the West Indian Centre since he was a teenager. He also does the afternoon slot on Saturdays on the local pirate station, Real Reggae FM and has quite a reputation on the DJing circuit.

"Ask Mixer when Skin and Bones coming to put in the new boiler," Uncle Al said.

Michael has identical twin brothers called Skin and Bones – I kid you not. One is an electrician and the other a plumber. Michael is a builder so they have their own business. Those aren't their real names of course. Their real names are Matthew and Mark but only Portia, their mum call them that. I didn't believe Michael that they got their nicknames because they were really skinny as kids until I saw a school photograph of them when they were about ten years old. If they had stood sideways, the photographer would have had trouble seeing them. They looked like two little stick kids with long necks and pin heads.

Looking at them now it's hard to believe. Michael goes to the gym every now and then and drags me with him but Skin and Bones work out constantly. They are both bouncers part-time and are so muscle bound they have to walk through doors sideways. Michael also has a brother called Luke. I think Portia was going for a full house with the four gospels but then she had a girl, so she called her Joan.

"Uncle Al, I made red pea soup for dinner. Why don't you go and get some?" I said pointedly as I looked at Ferdie sitting in the chair. His sense of humour and Uncle Al's naivety had got them into countless amounts of trouble over the years. I'd never seen Ferdie looking so depressed. He seemed to have shrunk within himself.

"No, mi eat dinner already," Uncle Al replied.

"Well get yourself a drink then," I said trying to wink at him without Ferdie seeing.

Uncle Al stared at me with a confused frown.

"A don't... want a drink. Why your eye twitching like that? You need to get something for your nerves, girl."

I groaned inwardly. "Stupid man!" I thought.

"Actually, Kelly, I'll have a drink of water," Ferdie said, "but I'll just use your toilet first."

As Ferdie closed the door, I pounced on Uncle Al.

"Uncle, what's the matter with you?" I hissed. "Have you never heard of confidentiality? Can't you take a hint?"

Uncle Al's face was a picture as the penny dropped.

"Oh Lord! Kelly, me sorry, man! You should have told me."

"Okay, never mind. Just bring Ferdie a drink and make yourself scarce so I can talk to him in private."

"Okay but Kelly, yu know me is a simple man. Mi can't bother with the coat and dagger business."

"Cloak," I corrected.

"What?"

"Never mind, Uncle."

"Ferdie needs to let Babsie know who wears the trousers in that house."

"Like you do with Aunty Bliss, you mean?"

"Yes! Er... no, no man. Wha'appen to yu, Kelly? You know Bliss is another kettle of crab all together."

"You mean fish."

"No... I mean crab," he answered. "She's claiming I know 'bout things I don't know anything about."

"Ferdie and Babsie?" I asked.

"Mmm. Ferdie and I go way back... since we were little boys wearing short pants in Jamaica. He's got my back, I've got his, but I ask you, how can Ferdie lead me astray if I don't want to be led?"

Just then, Ferdie came back looking apologetic. Uncle Al made a hasty retreat while Ferdie drank the glass of water without stopping. He put the glass down with a heavy sigh.

"A might as well just pour the water straight into the toilet for as soon as I have a drink I have to run to the toilet to peepy."

"Really?" I said thoughtfully. "What do you want to talk to me about why you have to come round at this time of night?"

Ferdie sighed again. "I'm in big trouble, Kelly. Babsie threatening to divorce me because she thinks I'm having an affair."

"Is there any reason why she should think that?" I asked as innocently as I could.

"No."

Babsie had almost been in tears as she confided in me that she suspected Ferdie was seeing someone else. She said he had been acting suspiciously recently and their love life had taken a dive. In fact, it had dived and was "lying motionless at the bottom of the pool", were Babsie's exact words.

"Come on, Ferdie, she must have a reason," I coaxed.

Ferdie cleared his throat and shuffled his feet like a little boy caught with his hand in the biscuit jar.

"'Cos de dragon don't walk de trail no more, man," he said quietly.

Now I pride myself on being good at working out cryptic clues but this one had me. I looked at him blankly.

"You know..." he said.

I shook my head.

"That calypso song," he said, nodding in the direction of his crotch. "The old gentleman gone to sleep."

"Oh..." I said as understanding dawned. "I see..."

Ferdie looked as if he wanted the floor to swallow him up. I nodded encouragingly for him to continue.

"On my birthday Babsie dressed up real nice in her baby doll nightdress with the matching panties without the –"

"Yes, I get the picture!" I cut in. It was one thing to want details but I didn't think I could handle the details if they were too graphic and coming from a man old enough to be my father.

"Em… sorry, I was getting a bit carried away" Ferdie said sheepishly. "Anyway Babsie said she wanted to give me a special present. The old gentleman only raise his head a little and then went back to sleep. Babsie was real understanding. She said it was that rum Mixer gave me. Since then, the old dragon dead, Kelly. Him gone limp like lettuce."

"What do you think the problem could be?" I asked.

"Well, I was talking to one of the lads at work and he said a friend of his had the same trouble…"

"And?"

"They buried him last month."

"Now, don't go jumping to conclusions. It could be anything."

"No, it's me prostrate… the big C. I'm not afraid to go. I've made my will but I don't know how to tell Babsie."

"If it is your prostate, don't you think you should go and see your doctor before you plan your funeral?"

"Yu mad! That little slip of a girl look like she just finish school. I can't discuss man business with her!"

"But you're talking to me about it."

"That's different. You're not a woman, you're family."

"Thank you," I said.

"No…no… sorry. Of course you're a woman and a very nice one but –"

"It's all right." I smiled at him. No point making him feel even more depressed than he already was. "I see you've changed your glasses."

"The old ones were useless. I let Babsie buy a dress for two hundred pounds because I couldn't see the price tag properly."

I had to stifle the smile this time because Cousin Babsie had already shared the joke with me.

"I just need to use your toilet again, Kelly, and get another drink."

Uncle Al nearly fell into the room when Ferdie opened the door.

"A was just coming to see if Ferdie want a beer," he said.

"No," I said. "Definitely no beer but you can get him another glass of water, please." I'd begun to suspect what Ferdie's problem was.

The next day, I made Ferdie an appointment to see the practice nurse at his doctor's surgery. She tested his glucose levels, then sent him to the hospital for further blood tests, which confirmed that he had diabetes. The medication he was prescribed, I found out later, woke the old dragon up a treat.

Ferdie took Babsie away for the weekend recently. From the big smile Babsie came back with, I'd say the dragon is definitely walking the trail again.

DE TING

When I was growing up in Jamaica, people rarely referred to money by name. It was always 'de t'ing' or 'de somet'ing'. My grandmother would say,

"Chile, come tek de pardner money fi mi."

It was all right to mention the 'm' word because there was no-one else around. "When yu pass Breda Joseph," she would continue, "call to him and ask him to give yu de t'ing. No go ina di yard far him ha two fool fool daag de wi bite yu. Then pass by Sista Gwen and ask har fi give yu fi har t'ing to."

And I would look at my grandmother in total confusion. I had spent my first years in Kingston with my mother before she immigrated to England and was still getting the hang of patois. I would ask, "What ting yu mean, Granny?" She would give me 'the look' and answer, "Never yu mind, just gwaan. Walk good and no go dash it weh a bush."

Sometimes if I asked too many questions, she would bend down looking around for what she called a switch, which was a small stick, as if to beat me and say,

"But Lord, yu see me dying trial. Yu maddah gaan a England an lef yu here fi give me nothing but trouble. Chile, go weh from me, yu name pickny."

I would skip away smartly, knowing I'd gone too far although in all the years I lived with my grandmother I don't remember her once beating me.

So I would walk up the dirt track from our little wooden house next to the family cemetery, the burying ground to us. I would idly beat the heads off the flowering weeds or bush as it was called with a stick, making the butterflies and moths fly out and deliberately rake up the dust with my sandals. I would stop for a little while by the big mango tree where the pigs hung out, watching them feasting on the rotten mangoes in the mud their feet had churned up. I loved to see the old black and white sow as she lay with her back against the tree while the tiny pink piglets fed hungrily, their little curly tails in the air. I would pass the giant avocado pear tree with half its roots exposed providing a shelter for animals at night. I never liked passing that point alone. It always had a strong animal smell. The sun never seemed to quite reach that bit of the track. It had a cold, gloomy feel that always made my head raise and made me shiver as I hurried past afraid to look into the hollow in case I saw something I didn't want to see. The red eye rolling calf perhaps or the one foot man with his back to front head - tales I had over heard my older cousins telling late at night long after I had been sent to bed.

I would come out into the bright sunshine again and see the grey smoke curling lazily from Brother Joseph's kitchen further down the hill. I knew better than to just walk into his yard even though there was no fence or gate. I would stand by the June plum tree and shout, "Breda Jo!" The dogs would immediately start to bark furiously.

"Breda Jo," I would call again. "Hold daag!"

The old man with his bow legs would appear on his veranda, leaning on his walking stick and peering short-sightedly over his spectacles to see who it was while the dogs stood beside him barking frantically. He would always have his open bible in his hand.

"A who dat?" he would ask.

"A mi, Miss Bea granddaughter, sah!" I would shout above the dogs.

"A who?" he would shout again, aiming a kick at the nearest dog which was never anywhere near it, for everyone knew he loved and fed those dogs better than himself and wouldn't harm a hair on their heads. "Daag, goh sid dung!" he would shout and the two dogs would immediately drop to their stomachs, heads on paws, whining and wagging their tails. I can see them now, trying to shuffle forward on their stomachs when they thought he wasn't looking. One was called Brown Dog and the other Black Dog. Yes... I know, but it made perfect sense at the time to me.

"Come, come in, dem nah trouble yu," he would say. Putting down his open bible on his rocking chair, he would hobble down the steps of the veranda. The steps were made of huge undressed logs cut in half and nailed together with smaller logs at the sides. Brother Joseph's house was built on stilts at the back and had large boulders underneath wedging it into the hill. In the space underneath, commonly known as 'house bottom' as opposed to the roof which was 'house top', taking advantage of the shade from the scorching sun were a nanny goat with two kids and a couple of fat red hens.

"Oh, a yu Kelly. Yu come fi di t'ing? Ah right, wait deh soh likkle."

He would go back into the house while the dogs watched me suspiciously, making the odd low growl just to remind me that I was in their territory. Brother Joseph would emerge a few minutes later with an old tartan kerchief carefully wrapped up and tied with string which he handed to me.

"Wait, wait deh, mi have somet'ing fi yu granmaddah." He would go into the other smaller shack in the yard which served as his kitchen from which the smell of spicy cornmeal porridge wafted. The smell of rich coconut milk, nutmeg and bay leaves would fill my nostrils. He would come out again carrying a crocus bag. Depending on what was in season, it usually contained mangoes, sometimes callaloo, a piece of yam or pumpkin or even sweet corn. Those were the days before the big supermarkets, ASDA and Tesco, when fruit and vegetables didn't have to comply with European regulations and had seasons.

"Tank yu sah," I would say. Just as I was walking out of the yard, he would see the disappointed look on my face and say,

"Wait a minute, chile." I would stand and wait patiently, trying to suppress my smile because I knew what was coming. He would go back into the house and come back with a toffee which we called stagaback or a round red and white mint. If he didn't have any, he would slowly walk round to the side of the kitchen for his crook stick, then, he would walk to the mango tree and holding the stick in one hand shake down a ripe mango, catching it deftly in his other hand. Smiling he would hand it to me.

"Say 'howdido' to yu granmaddah fi me," he would say.

"Yes sah," I would answer already digging my teeth into the warm thick skin of the mango.

"Ah right," he would say like my grandmother, "gwaan now and walk good. Noh goh trow weh de money a bush."

"No sah, mi nah do dat," I would answer.

I would hum to myself, tucking into my mango as I skipped along the track to Sister Gwen's house. I would pull down the wide brim straw hat over my face which my wise grandmother had put on my head, feeling the hot sun on my back, believing life was good for a six year old girl.

A LITTLE KNOWLEDGE IS
A DANGEROUS THING

Last year, we went to Jamaica on a family holiday but we, well some of us anyway, very nearly didn't get there.

It was just supposed to have been me, my girls, their partners (Shari's husband Omar and baby Issy of course and Lolly's boyfriend, Steven). Yes, I said, Lolly's boyfriend – nice boy but I'll tell you about my traumatic transformation over the boyfriend in a minute. It involved being dragged, kicking and screaming into the 21st Century I might add.

The holiday was to celebrate my 50th and Issy's 1st birthday. My grandson was born on my birthday – how good is that! Then Aunty Bliss, you remember her, otherwise known as Beverley, decided that she wanted to go too.

Of course, Uncle Al, Aunty Bliss' husband, doesn't go anywhere without Cousin Babsie's husband, Ferdie. And, once they decided that they were going, my mother decided she wasn't going to be left behind. Then it sort of … escalated. So, that was how I came to be in the travel agents in Chorlton booking fifteen seats to Jamaica.

Anyway, I'd been home for two hours. I had acquired a few more grey hairs, trying to explain to the woman in the travel agents exactly what I wanted, before Lolly told me Aunty Bliss had phoned and left a message for me to ring her urgently, as soon as I got in.

"So why are you only telling me now?" I asked the teenager.

"I left a message on your mobile," Lolly answered. She knows my mobile phone lives in the bottom of my handbag and I never hear it ring.

Well, you should know what I'm like by now. Before I'd finished dialling Aunty Bliss' number, I'd imagined a funeral, made a mental note to take my black skirt to the dry cleaners and matched up a couple of wedding outfits in my head.

"Didn't she say what it was about, Laura?" I asked, incredulous, that an eighteen year old hadn't yet grasped the concept of 'urgency'.

"No, she was shouting something about killing Cousin Babsie."

Okay... so it's going to be a funeral then, I thought.

There was a knock at the door, which Lolly with her ipod plugged into her ears ignored. I hadn't been goal shooter in the netball team at school for nothing and the rolled up tea towel got her in the back of the head.

"What?" she asked rubbing her head. "Aww!" I shook my fist at her.

"I was going," she said as I pointed to the door. "One of these days, I'll phone Childline!" she shouted from the hall.

Auntie Bliss and my Cousin Myra's daughter, Tiana or Tootsie as we call her exploded into the hallway.

"Kelly, wha'appen to yu man? Yu nuh know wha urgent mean?"

My aunt walked into my kitchen and switched on the kettle. Then she opened the cupboard got out mugs and sugar while I sat open mouthed with the ringing phone still in my hand.

"You're not at home then, Aunty Bliss. You're here." She gave me a withering look.

"Don't mind me," I said. "Come on in and make yourself comfortable." Sarcasm was completely lost on my aunt.

"Do you want coffee?" she asked, getting the milk from the fridge.

"Er... actually... yes please."

I grabbed hold of the mug which had started jumping across the kitchen table in time to the base of the music now coming from upstairs. Before I could shout, Lolly's head appeared around the door.

"It's not me, look, I'm listening to my ipod," she said. Hands on her hips, Aunty Bliss marched to the bottom of the stairs.

"Tiana! If you want to mek noise, goh to yu own house!" she bellowed. The music stopped in mid boom. "Yes, Aunty! Sorry!" the shout came back.

"Kelly, Babsie say she nah go a Jamaica again," Aunty Bliss said coming back into the kitchen. "Yu have any biscuits?"

"Why?" I asked, pointing to the tin on top of the fridge.

"It's true what yu always saying yu know, Kelly, a little knowledge is a damn dangerous t'ing."

"What do you mean?" I asked. "Am I always saying that?"

"It's all Ferdie's fault." It usually was, even when it wasn't.

"Why is it Ferdie's fault?" I asked.

"He was the one who told Babsie that she should take an interest in current affairs. Current affairs? I ask yu.... Wha wrong wid cake decorating? That's why she started buying The Jamaica Gleaner. She would be better off learning to cook!" I nearly choked trying to stifle a laugh. Babsie's brown stew salt fish was infamous. They have the fattest dog and cat in Manchester because Ferdie and the kids give them their food when Babsie isn't looking.

"Aunty Bliss, what has all this got to do with Babsie not going to Jamaica?"

"Well Babsie was following the career of the Prime Minister of Jamaica. You know she is the first female Prime Minister we've ever had."

"Yes, I know."

"Babsie's got a big scrap book with newspaper cuttings and everything."

"Really? I never knew Babsie had any interest in politics. She never votes!"

"Well she's also been following the recent elections in Jamaica and Portia Simpson-Miller, from the People's National Party, just lost. Bruce Golding, Jamaica Labour Party, won. Now Babsie is saying she's not going to spend her hard earned money in any country where dem fool fool enough to vote out dem first female Prime Minister so soon."

"You're joking!"

Aunty bliss gave me a withering look. "Kelly, me look like mi a joke? Of course, if Babsie nah goh, then Ferdie nah goh either and you know Ferdie and my Al are joined at the hip. Al say him nah goh if Ferdie nah goh. And how mi fi goh widout Al? Who a goh chase weh the lizard dem and di big 'ol dirty bullfrogs? Now you tell me that, Kelly?"

I had no answer so I reached for a couple of chocolate biscuits and put a bit more coffee in my mug. I suddenly felt the need of a strong caffeine fix.

We called a family conference. Everyone sat around my extended kitchen table with Mum, Uncle Al, Ferdie and Cousin Babsie playing a game of dominoes.

"The PNP was in power for eighteen years, just like Maggie Thatcher," Mum said, scratching her ear. A diversionary tactic, as she tried to get a sneaky look at Ferdie's dominoes. "Why Portia make dem get rid of her after only one term in office Lord only know?"

"Who's Maggie Thatcher, Grandma?" Lolly asked.

Mum looked at her. "Child, do you only go to school to eat the dinner? They're not teaching you anything."

"She was the first British female Prime Minister, Lolly," my brother JJ answered.

"I'm not at school anymore Grandma; I'm at college," Lolly answered.

"Yes, even more reason why you should have learnt something by now."

"Mum..." I said.

"What? Lolly knows I'm only joking. Don't you Lols? I know she got all 'A's and 'B's in her GCSEs; my clever girl. I wonder where she got her brain from?" she added looking at me.

"If you want my opinion," Mum continued, "Portia waited too

long to call an election". JJ and I looked at Mum then at each other with raised eyebrows.

"I had no idea you knew anything about British politics, Mum, never mind Jamaican politics," JJ said. Mum gave one of her mischievous chuckles.

"I'm old, boy, but I'm not cold yet," she said.

"Put it here, girl!" Aunty Bliss shouted, squealing with laughter as she held up her hand to exchange a high five with Mum. Their laughter was so infectious that we all joined in.

"Since John Joseph bought me the computer for my birthday I've been surfing the net. I listen to Radio Jamaica on the internet all the time," Mum said.

"Best thing I ever bought you eh Mum," JJ said. Mum was the only one who called him by his full name.

"Grandma's a silver surfer," Lolly laughed.

"A what? A silver server? I thought that was a posh waitress," Cousin Babsie said.

"Surfer, Babsie, not server," Uncle Al said. "You know old grey haired people like you who use the internet."

Babsie looked at him with narrowed eyes. "Look 'ere Al, don't let me have to tell yu exactly where yu can find more grey hair than on my head." Mum cut in as Uncle Al was about to answer.

"Now you two, don't start! You're not too old for me to give you a slap." Babsie and Uncle Al glared at each other across the table but didn't say anything else. Lolly and Tootsie couldn't stop laughing. The rest of us didn't laugh because we weren't too sure Mum was joking.

"Lolly, when are you coming to show me how to rip and burn my CDs?" Mum asked, defusing the situation. "I've downloaded some of the ones I want already," she added slamming her dominoes onto the table.

"Hee hee hee! Mi win again!" Mum got up and did a little victory jig around the kitchen before gathering up the heap of cashew nuts on the table that they were playing for. I felt as if I'd just fallen into a parallel universe.

"Hello...people... can we just get back to the business in hand, please," I said. I turned to cousin Babsie in desperation.

"Babsie, are you sure you don't want to go to Jamaica? That's a lot of money we're going to lose. We got a special deal because there were so many of us."

"Money isn't everything, Kelly. That's what you're always saying."

"That's because a noh fi yu money," I heard Ferdie mutter under his breath.

Me and my big mouth! I decided that I was going to have to watch what I said in future. I had no idea my family took so much notice of the things I say.

"Cousin Babsie, money isn't everything but we're talking about fifteen Air Jamaica seats at £500 a throw," JJ said patiently.

"Well... yu can all goh without me, you know, JJ," Babsie said in a quiet pitiful voice. "I'll stay here... all by myself." She looked at Ferdie. "Yu can goh too if yu want, yu hear Ferdie?"

Ferdie looked up nervously at everyone and back to his dominoes. We all heard Cousin Babsie's unspoken words loud and clear ... Go if you're ready to die.

"No, no Baby," Ferdie answered. "You know I could never do that." There was a collective sigh of relief.

We debated into the small hours by which time, the men had consumed the half bottle of Wray and Nephew over proof rum which I had been saving for my Christmas cake, and a dozen red strip beers. Mum had fried a huge batch of dumplings to go with her new recipe of chicken in red wine. I only had some sherry so after she and Aunty Bliss had tasted a few glasses to make sure it would be all right, they said, they poured the rest over the chicken. This was after they had laced Cousin Babsie's black current juice with a generous measure.

Finally, we got the holiday back on track. Lolly, bless her, found a photograph of the Jamaican Prime Minister, Bruce Golding, on the internet and showed it to Cousin Babsie. It was love at first sight. She said he reminded her of Yellow Man, one of her favourite reggae singers. I couldn't see the likeness myself.

Cousin Babsie's change of heart could also have had something to do with the conversation I overheard her having with my mother.

"But dem woman ya noh have no sense," Mum said.

"How yu mean?"

"Well…if Portia Simpson-Miller did have any sense, the first thing she would have done when she was elected Prime Minister was to call a summit with Margaret Thatcher, Benizir Bhuto and Condilisa Rice."

I pricked up my ears and listened. This was going to be good.

"But Aunty," Babsie said, " Maggie Thatcher is a pensioner now and Benizir Bhuto is dead."

"Yes, a know but, if Portia did have any sense at the time, she would have called a summit, cooked them some good ackee and salt fish with yam and bananas and exchange some tips on how to sort out de damn fool fool man dem."

"But Aunty Condilisa Rice isn't –"

"No, no, listen noh man." Mum chuckled. I could hear the mischief in her voice. "Portia could have got Maggie to bring some fish and chips and Benizir to bring a curry. Nothing with too much pepper… you know a nice chicken balti or something. Condilisa would have had to bring McDonald's because she noh look like she ever cook anything in har little skinny life." They both burst out laughing. Smiling and shaking my head, I tiptoed quietly away.

Cousin Babsie decided she wanted to go to Jamaica so that she could meet Bruce Golding in person. We didn't enlighten her on the odds of that happening. I heard Ferdie kiss his teeth as he threw his copy of The Jamaica Gleaner in the bin before he left.

Oh, I was going to tell you about Lolly's boyfriend, Steven. Well, call me old fashion but I won't let him stay overnight at our house so when Lolly said he'd never been on an aeroplane and ask if he could come with us on holiday, my immediate answer was – hell no!

But Lolly enlisted the aid of the demon lawyer – her sister Charlotte, and they worked on me for days, putting their arguments for the defence. Let's just say that I never ever want to be cross examined by Shari in court. She'd have me pleading guilty to crimes I'd never even heard of just to shut her up.

Anyway 'the boyfriend' came on holiday with us and I survived the experience - just. After having so many girls around me, it was a pleasant change to see things from the teenage male perspective. They never figured out how the baby's toy that shouts 'halt who goes there' when anyone goes within three feet of it, found its way outside Lolly's bedroom door every night. Steven is actually a lovely boy – he spends five minutes in the bathroom without finishing off all my toiletries, he's low maintenance when it comes to shopping and very useful for carrying bags. I hear his mother has just had another baby boy, so I'm thinking of asking her if she'll swap Steve for one of my girls.

BABSIE'S BIRTHDAY

Last year my cousin Barbara or Babsie as we call her, had a milestone birthday. After guarding her age like a national secret for decades and only telling people that she was twenty-one plus a few, she suddenly had a need to tell anyone who would listen and many who didn't want to, that she was approaching the big 'five O'. She made it clear that she wanted her birthday to be memorable but we didn't realise just how memorable it would be.

Babsie booked the West Indian Community Centre, complete with caterers for the day. She sent out at least a hundred gilt edged invitations and hired a white stretch limousine.

"Ferdie a goh have to get a second job to pay for all that," Uncle Al remarked, laughing, when he dropped off our invitation. "Now my Bliss getting upset because she seh all she got for her fiftieth was a meal. I didn't hear her complaining at the time. Those flowers I gave her cost a fortune!"

"Uncle, you told me your friend Mohammed got them wholesale for you from the market."

"Shush man! Shush! How yu mout so big , Kelly? Yu want Bliss to hear you?" He looked back at my Aunty Beverley (Bliss) in the car and smiled. I waved innocently. Aunty Bliss looked suspiciously at both of us and waved back hesitantly.

So, the great day dawned, overcast with threatening rain… typical Mancunian weather. The white limo after taking us on a small tour of the city; ASDA supermarket, the community garden centre, the building site now moth balled because of the recession and the council housing estate, slowly made it's way along the high street towards the West Indian Community Centre. The Polish driver chatted to us cheerfully although we couldn't really hear or understand most of what he was saying.

"You go have de nice time…yes?" he asked, nodding at me in the rear view mirror. I nodded.

"Very good. I practice my English…you don't mind? He's good, yes?" I nodded again. "Yeah, it's ok." I said. "At least you speak English, I can't speak Polish."

"Yes…yes…very good!" he laughed.

"Noh encourage him, Kelly," Ferdie said grumpily, "Cos him noh even a look where him a goh."

All went well, although we did pass hair-raisingly close to a few parked cars, until we came to turn into Westwood Street, where the West Indian Centre is. The limo got stuck! By the time the driver realised that he definitely wasn't going to make the corner, a line of traffic had formed behind him and he couldn't reverse.

"No worry…is no problem… I fix her in a small jiffy," he said but his smile had slipped a bit.

After about five minutes of churning up the grass on the corner, the driver jumped out and opened the door for us.

"I sorry… maybe is best you walk… is no far. Look… is only pebbles throw."

We weren't happy but we were beginning to see the sense in his suggestion. The kids, Ferdie and I all got out easily enough. Then came Babsie in her gold lamee gown with matching shoes and handbag, long white gloves and…golden tiara on her head. By now people were stopping to see what was going on. I think they thought it must be a celebrity arriving. Ferdie looked a little uncomfortable in the morning suit with gold quilted waistcoat which Babsie had made him wear. His black patent leather shoes glistened in competition with the gold rings and heavy chains on his wrists. Maybe that was why he was wearing dark glasses even though there was no sun in sight.

A group of Chinese people in a car started taking photographs.

The other motorists looked on, bemused. Some drivers further down the queue of traffic who couldn't see what was happening started blowing their horns. The strong smell of hops from the brewery across the road pervaded the air.

Two community police officers on bicycles watched us from a safe distance further down the road, looking unsure if they should intervene.

At this point I think Ferdie decided that he might as well 'style it out', so sticking out his chest as proud as a peacock, he held out his arm for Babsie as she stepped out of the limousine. She tottered alarmingly on her high heels, before gaining her balance.

"Me did tell yu noh fi buy dem high heel shoes deh, yu know Babsie. Why yu don' listen to me, man? Yu a goh bruk yu neck ina dem."

"Shut up, man. After yu noh know nothing 'bout fashion. Kelly, walk pon de other side of mi so mi can hold on to yu before mi fall down in front a all dem people ya."

I dutifully obliged, wishing I was somewhere else as I tried to ignore the increasing crowd of curious shoppers who were stopping to have a good look at us. I felt ashamed of myself when Babsie whispered nervously to me.

"Lord, dem all looking at mi. Mi look all right, Kelly? A think I overdid it a bit, don't? Maybe a shouldn't have put in the gold extensions."

I was about to agree when I looked at Babsie's face pleading for reassurance. Her make up had been immaculately done by one of her daughters and my eldest daughter, Shari. Babsie has that dark, smooth complexion which some black women are blessed with. Even close up her skin looked like velvet. The truth was, she actually looked stunning! Moss Side with its bad reputation of gangs and shootings, which made the headlines every week, had never seen the like. I doubt if it ever would again. I looked back to see the Limousine still blocking the road and an increasing line of traffic forming. People had wound their windows down and were trying to see what was going on.

One of the two community police officers was now getting the cars to reverse while the other directed the limousine's driver as he tried to reverse in order to negotiate the bend.

"Babs, you look gorgeous...like a real African queen," I answered, giving her arm a squeeze. Babsie's face lit up with a beaming gold tooth smile that made her look ten years younger than her fifty years. She pulled herself up to her full height in her six inch heels. And bwoy did she look tall. We don't come from a family of short women. With me on one side and Ferdie on the other holding her up, she sashayed like a catwalk model the rest of the way down the street and into the West Indian Community Centre to rapturous applause from all the family and her friends and Stevie Wonder's 'Happy Birthday To You'.

As I went through the door, I caught sight of Cousin Dexter's food van, 'Rice n Spice', parked in a corner of the car park with a queue of kids buying burgers and chips. Dexter was always one for seizing an opportunity.

My partner, Michael, better known as Mixer was the Master of Ceremonies. He is the resident DJ at the West Indian Centre but had taken time off today out of the DJ's box. After welcoming everyone and thanking them for coming, he made the big mistake of asking for a couple of people to say a few words. He really should have known better and handpicked the speakers. An hour later he was still trying to get the microphone away from people. The final straw was when Babsie's friend, who had obviously had more than one glass of punch, gave her speech then decided to join in with Stevie Wonder in the background singing 'Isn't She Lovely'. She was going for her third song before Michael managed to wrestle the microphone from her.

Babsie and Ferdie's youngest son, Richie, gave a lovely speech praising his mother. It brought a lump to my throat but maybe he should have left out the bit about his mother wearing her knickers on her head in the shower instead of a shower cap, even though it had everyone rolling about laughing. I could tell Babsie was very moved. When Richie had finished, to loud applause and shouts of "Bless him Lord!", Babsie beckoned him round the corner by the kitchen. With practiced precision Richie ducked the slap she aimed at his head, in the middle of hugging and kissing him with tears threatening to spoil her make-up.

Eventually everybody brought their presents and cards and presented them to Babsie who was sitting at the top table with her family like at a wedding. In the middle of the table was a huge six tier birthday cake, specially made by Cousin Myra. My made a killing that day with Christmas cake orders. It's a good thing there was no-one with epilepsy present or the relentless flashes and clicks of cameras and mobile phones would have probably given them a seizure. Babsie just sat like Lewis Carol's Cheshire cat, grinning from ear to ear as she basked in her moment of glory.

After Michael had read the telegrams from relatives in America and Jamaica, we closed the curtains and turned off the lights for a slide show put together by Babsie and Ferdie's kids. It got a lot of 'oohs!' and 'aaws!' and the usual hysterical laughter. The slide show started with pictures of Babsie as a little girl in Jamaica, then there was one of the yellowing photo in her expired Jamaican passport taken when she was nine with two massive ribbons bigger than her head. Her teenage years in hot pants, big afro hair style and platform shoes had everyone falling about, laughing. There was a chorus of wolf whistles and applause. An anonymous male voice from the back shouted -

"Gwan girl! Yu still have dem sexy legs!" Ferdie with an annoyed look was straining his neck to see who it was until Babsie dug him hard in his ribs with her elbow. Then a picture of Babsie and Ferdie in their early twenties came up. They turned and smiled at each other and I saw Ferdie squeeze her hand. Ferdie had the biggest afro I have ever seen that was hiding half of Babsie's face. His collar and tight fitting flared trousers were wide enough to fly with. There was a piercing whistle from somewhere. Another voice, this time a woman, shouted –

"Gwan Superfly! But where di hair gaan?" Everyone burst out laughing again.

Then came pictures of the wedding and the kids as each new addition came along. They brought back memories for everyone present who I'm sure had similar pictures at home. A few women had to get tissues out while the men cleared their throats.

After the slide show, Michael asked Cousin Myra to bless the table. I'm not against thanking God for my blessings but the caterers began to look very worried as they struggled to keep the food hot without it burning. Someone's mobile phone kept going off while My was praying but that was dealt with by a loud kissing of teeth and a voice which shouted -

"Cum out a here wid dat man…wha'appen to yu! Yu noh hav noh respect!" I think it might have been Aunty Bliss.

Cousin My really got into full swing with the prayer and I thought she was going to get into the spirit but then I think we had some divine intervention. The microphone she was using suddenly went dead. All heads turned towards the DJ's box where all the sound equipment was. Michael's identical twin brothers, Matthew and Mark, better known as Skin and Bones who were on temporary DJ duty were pointing at each other. One of them had accidentally touched a switch. My started beating the microphone against her hand.

"It dead already, man yu caan kill it noh more," Uncle Al said.

The people out in the hallway thought the prayer had ended without them realising and shouted "Amen!" so Cousin My had to just leave it there.

While we were eating, my mum, who just can't help herself, spotted the two community police officers hovering outside on their bicycles, having sent the limousine on it's way and restored order to the Saturday afternoon traffic.

"Poor t'ing. It cold out there and dem look hungry," she said, beckoning frantically to them through the window. They refused her invitation to come in because they were on duty they said, but mum insisted that they came round to the back door of the Community Centre.

After enquiring whether they liked West Indian food, my mother piled two plates high with a variety of food and brought two chairs out for the officers to sit on under the awnings. To the amusement of the catering staff, mum also insisted that they had to come in and wash their hands before eating and say grace, which they obediently did. She took a third chair outside and while they ate she gave them her thoughts on where the police were going wrong on the policing of the area. They seemed genuinely interested in what she had to say, so we just left her to it. A group of youths who had been kicking a beer can around the car park, gathered to listen and seemed suitably impressed, adding their comments to what mum said.

Mum is now on first name terms with Darren and Phil and told them anytime they were passing her house they should pop in for a cup of tea. They also left with an invitation from the Centre Manager to come and talk to the Youth Club about bicycle maintenance. Mum wrapped up two little parcels of cake as they were leaving which she gave them to take home for their wives. That day the police, with mum's help, scored a huge point for community relations.

I don't know if it was just a slow news week or if we really did make that much of an impression, because the next day, there was Babsie, gold tooth sparkling and the limo stuck on the corner of Westwood Street, splashed all over the front page of not one but two of the local newspapers. There was also a photograph of mum linking arms with the two community police officers. It's just as well they were all smiling otherwise it would have looked as if she was being arrested. Fortunately, the photograph of me wasn't that clear so I can deny ever being there.

OLE AGE NUH NICE

"Lawd, but ole age nuh nice," I remember my grandmother saying many times as she rubbed her aching back or knees, or called me to thread or 'tring her sewing needle because her eyesight was bad. I didn't really understand what my grandmother meant at the time, but in recent years, perhaps because I'm heading there faster than I would like to, I remember those words and they have come to have real meaning for me.

I remember saying one day when I was annoyed at being called away from my game to thread yet another needle, "Young age nuh nice either, Granny." Granny chuckled under her breath and said, "Never mind, Baby, gwaan."

Last year we had a number of deaths in our family, one after the other. They had all reached a ripe old age but I just never noticed them getting old. One day they were young and loud and full of life, the next they were old, still loud but feeble. Age had just crept up on them.

My Aunt Gwenda died after a long illness during which she lost so much weight she was barely recognisable. When I visited her, after not seeing her for a couple of weeks, she looked me up and down and said,

"Kelly, a so yu gaan fat."

I already knew I'd gone fat because a few days earlier my mother had said to me with her trade mark laugh, "Hee hee hee! Kelly yu fat so 'til even yu head fat."

That's the thing about old black people I find, and my mother in particular, they don't mince words – tact is not a word in their dictionary. They just tell it like it is. Despite my best efforts, I'd gradually put on weight as I had got older because, "ole age nuh nice", as Granny used to say but my mother and aunt didn't do anything for my self esteem. Unlike my lovely brother, John Joseph (JJ to us). When I complained to him about my double chin, he gave me a big bear hug and said, "No man, yu nuh fat. You're just a good armful." Bless him. I knew I would be rewarded one day for not putting that spider down his pants when he was six.

Aunt Gwenda redeemed herself when she added, " A wish mi did still fat soh. When mi a your age – when mi was young, a so mi did fat an' pretty. Mi would an give anyt'ing fi tek off some of di weight. Now mi would an' give anyt'ing fi put on some weight fi cover mi little bird leg dem." She definitely redeemed herself as I was approaching a significant milestone birthday. Just like mum, she laughed that 'hee hee hee!' laugh that goes up at the end. The one that older black people do so well, that is so infectious you have to join in and laugh too.

Isn't it funny how our perceptions are different and change with time and culture. To me being fat was an unhealthy and negative thing but to my seriously ill aunt and her generation, being fat was associated with being attractive and healthy.

Before Aunt Gwenda became ill, she was a big woman – described as 'trapling' by my mum. The Oxford English Dictionary says 'strapping' but personally, I think 'trapling' is a much better description of most of the women in my family over a certain age. Old age and the ailments which came with it, reduced my aunt to a frail shadow and sharply brought home to me the passage of time and our mortality.

It was losing so many of my older relatives in a short space of time after having no deaths in our family for years, that made me suddenly notice that I was getting older. It became increasingly difficult to ignore my creaking knee joints. My greying hair became more noticeable and I had to start using hair dye out of necessity not fashion. I also began to be plagued with minor and some not so minor health problems.

I was diagnosed with high blood pressure and hot on its heels came diabetes. I thought my world was coming to an end when I had to give up rum cake but I drew the line at giving up bun 'n cheese completely. There are some things in life you just have to suffer for. Be warned all you young ones who think you can eat McDonald's for breakfast, lunch and dinner. The body needs fruit, vegetables and more fruit, washed down with large amounts of pure water... not cocoa cola or lemonade. I was once a size 12... honestly.

My doctor decided that while she was overhauling everything she might as well send me for a mammogram. The men who are reading this, you will never know how lucky you were to be born men so you can escape the dreaded mammogram. Believe you me, if you think ole age nuh nice, then trust me, mammograms aren't nice either. Nor is having doctors half your age poke and prod you like their kneading dough with their cold hands.

"How come dem doctor yah always look like dem noh start use razor yet?" remarked my cousin Barbara (Babsie), as we sat in the waiting room at the hospital. She had insisted on going with me for the X-ray to give me moral support. She said with a big smile, gold tooth flashing, that she was happy to provide moral support, but I'd have to buy a good bra for any other kind of support. I didn't laugh because I was honestly trying hard not to encourage her. Well all right then, I wasn't trying that hard because I needed cheering up. Babsie didn't need any encouragement though.

"Yu notice how dem rub dem hand together before dem examine yu?" she laughed.

"It's to warm them," I answered, grinning.

"Warm dem mi foot bottom! Kelly yu too innocent," she whispered. Her eyes followed one of the doctors as he walked past. "Why yu think all the Muslim women dem tek dem husband in wid dem? For protection! Well, all mi have fi say is, when you goh ina dat room wid dat little Denzil Washington look alike, if him start rub him hand dem an' lick him lip, yu better run."

I nearly choked as I tried not to laugh out loud in the crowded waiting room. I was still trying to stifle the smile as the nurse called my name.

I looked at the X-ray machine apprehensively and wondered who the hell invented such a thing – had to be a man... a very sadistic one. I know which part of his anatomy I'd like to squash in it if I ever find him.

Whoever would have thought you could squash a woman's breast paper thin in a vice without anaesthetic? Well, the flat chested woman operating the machine managed it with frightening efficiency, and she didn't warm her hands! Come to think of it maybe she didn't start off with a flat chest. Perhaps she was forced to have a mammogram too and now she's getting her revenged on womankind.

You would think that illness and death in my family would have brought me closer to God but it didn't – not at the time anyway. It made me question everything I believed. God and I have worked it out now though... well I've learnt which one of us is boss and it isn't me.

As usual my mother, aunt and cousins were on hand to give me advice, peppered with their special brand of humour.

"Hmm! Yu notice how some woman run up an' down when dem young and de minute dem reach a certain age and everyt'ing start to go south, dem discover God. Like seh God noh did dideh a wait pon dem ole bad self all de time," my Aunt Beverley, known as Bliss, remarked. "Mi noh mean yu you know, Kelly." I was really glad she clarified that.

The women had all gathered at my house. That usually spelled trouble, especially after a couple of glasses of apricot wine, but we always had a good laugh as we cooked or baked and danced around the kitchen with each other to Dennis Brown or Gregory Isaacs. The men had gone off somewhere... usually someone's house to watch football or cricket, drink too much and play dominoes.

"Yes," my mother answered. "Then dem start talk 'bout 'Sister I've found the Lord'. One a these days yu see, mi a goh seh to one a dem, 'Sister, He wasn't lost! You were!'"

We all burst out laughing.

"It's more likely God was hiding from dem yu mean!" Cousin Myra chipped in.

"Lord, Myra yu too bad!" Cousin Babsie cried, " but I know exactly what yu mean."

"Yeah man," Cousin My continued. "Suddenly it's the 3-d picture of blue eyed Jesus on the living room wall. Like anybody did tell dem seh Jesus have blue eyes."

"And the framed Lords Prayer or Last Supper on the kitchen wall," mum added.

"And every other blessed word out of dem mout' is followed by 'my Jesus' and nothing is as 'sweet as Jesus'.

"What's wrong with that?" I asked still laughing. "You lot want to behave yourselves and go to church more often. It wouldn't do you any harm."

I ducked as Babsie pulled a face and threw a couple of peanuts at me. "Mi tek my Ferdie a church last week, wha'appen to yu?"

"It was your friend's wedding Babsie. That doesn't count," My said.

"Yu right, Kelly, there is nothing wrong with loving The Lord, if it's genuine," mum said seriously, "but when the roll is called up yonder... hmm... some of us going to hear those very words from the Bible, 'depart from me I know you not'."

"Hmm... a true yu know Mala," Cousin My said to my mum. "We shouldn't joke about it."

"So what about de men dem?" Cousin Babsie asked.

Cousin My kissed her teeth. "Cho man, why yu have to bring dem into it when yu know say most a dem a idiot? As dem turn forty dem leave dem good good wife and gaan look for wha dem noh put down. Dem fool up the woman dem ina church an' say dem turn Christian 'til dem walk down the aisle. Then dem gwaan bad same way til dem carry dem ina church feet first in a box."

Mum reached over and patted Cousin My's hand. We all looked at each other but didn't say anything because poor My was speaking from personal experience.

"Yu damn right, ole age nuh nice, Kelly," Aunty Bliss said, trying to lighten the mood again. "A nuh just yu brain forget t'ings yu noh."

We waited for the explanation.

"When you get to a certain age, even yu hair turn fool fool an' forget where it's suppose to grow. Didn't you know that? If yu a man, it get up an' gallop way gaan off yu head wid just a little piece a hide round a yu neck back. An' if yu a woman, it start grow pon u chin an' yu top lip. It grow out a yu nose, an' if yu really bad lucky, it start grow pon u chest an' out a yu ears dem."

The room exploded in laughter.

"Wha'appen to yu? A true! Mi know a woman wid hair pon a chest like King Kong. An' it can't even behave good an' stay black fi disguise itself. It hav fi turn grey an' wave let everybody see it," she continued. "Yu ever see grey hair ina somebody nose before?"

"An' yu noh even need fi worry too much if yu noh hav a man because, if like my husband, him already run way wid someone half yu age fi goh find himself," My said.

"Why?" Babsie asked.

"cause wid all dat hair, yu probably turn into a man yuself," Cousin My said wiping her eyes.

We all had tears running down our faces laughing by this time as we tried to outdo each other with our tales of the problems of getting older.

"If all that isn't bad enough," I added, "your kids think it's their duty to introduce you to trendy foods like sushi."

"Soo shee? A wha' name soh, Missis?" Cousin My asked.

"Sushi, Myra – raw fish," Babsie chipped in. "Yu know… Japanese food. Me an' yu try it in town Kelly, don't? Dem wrap it up ina one little roll wid rice ina dis black leaf somet'ing.

"Seaweed," I said.

"Raw fish an' seaweed? Now Lord why would I want to eat raw fish when mi a noh seal? Mum asked.

"It noh taste bad, Aunty Mala," Babsie said. "It can eat."

"No Missis, give me some cris fry fish wid a little onion and sweet pepper cut up on top any day."

'Ole age nuh nice' but my family definitely make it bearable. Age has given me wisdom or something else, to question everything I know and believe and ask questions no-one seems to have the answers to.

'Ole age nuh nice' because these days I walk past the mirror and sometimes look into the eyes of a stranger. I ask myself when I changed so much and turned into this person. I opened my mouth to brush my teeth and suddenly after years of wondering, I know exactly what 'long in the tooth' means.

Standing in front of my bedroom mirror rubbing cocoa butter into my dry skin, I pulled in my stomach as I realised that if the actor Robin Williams got sick, I could be a body double for 'Mrs Doubtfire' without the props.

Reading glasses, pungent ointments and knee supports are not things old people have. They are things I have! My mother, that frail old dear with the razor sharp tongue who often tells you the same story two or three times, is only eighteen years older than I am!

My children now speak to me in that patient, and occasionally impatient, tone I've found myself using sometimes with my mother. Echoes of Granny, 'Kelly, don't spit in the sky, it will fall right back into your face'.

I've started to reminisce about the good old days of paraffin heaters and coal fires that everyone except our selective memories, knows were horrible. Those were the icy cold days when I first came to England and dreamed about back home, until I was finally earning enough to go back and discovered that I had become a foreigner in my country of birth. I am a citizen of a non-existent country in the middle of the Atlantic Ocean.

These days, I look out at my garden at plants bare of leaves and covered in snow and dream of early retirement under a golden benevolent sun, white sand and blue foam-flecked sea with sweet syrupy mangoes running down my chin.

Actually 'ole age nuh nice' but middle age is not so bad. I'm just off to the gym with Cousin Babsie. That gorgeous instructor in the tight shorts is going to show me how to use all the equipment again. I'm so forgetful these days... hee hee hee!

LOLLY'S HAUNTED HOUSE

When I was young – longer ago than my teenage daughter, Laura (Lolly) thinks, because she thinks I was born yesterday, Halloween was never a big thing in England. However, like everything else that happens across the pond, in that 'land of the free, home of the brave', known as the USA, Halloween has caught on in a big way. Like obesity and everyone having a personal therapist, it's almost compulsory to participate in it. These days it's big business in England, too, almost as commercialised as Christmas. We have witches' and ghouls' costumes in sizes to fit babies to grannies, large plastic spiders, terror-inducing masks and demon faces carved into pumpkins, and all things scary in the shops from about September. They appear on the shelves as soon as the last of the suntan lotions, sunburn creams and summer clothes are sold.

I'd always discouraged my children from taking part in anything to do with Halloween, explaining to them what witches and demons are all about – not things good upstanding Christians should take lightly. When the girls – Lolly and Charlotte (Shari) – were younger, I usually took them out to eat or to see a film with their own treats. This was so they wouldn't feel they were missing out as droves of children wondered the neighbourhood, scaring each other, old people and dogs as they knocked on doors in the dark.

Now the children are grown and each year it becomes more difficult not to get caught up in all the green and black face painting, dripping tomato ketchup fangs and candle burning. Every year I suffer the endless stream of small children, sometimes a whole week before Halloween, shouting "Trick or treat!" accompanied by adults hovering in the background. I am drawn a little more into it, each year, by their happy laughter and shouts of "Thank you lady!" when I do give them anything.

It used to be just sweets that were given out, but now many people give money and children can collect a tidy sum in an evening. This has resulted in a new trend developing in recent years. Last year I opened the door to a group of not-so-small 'children' dressed in very frightening costumes with cans of lager in their hands. As they stood menacingly on my doorstep, the trick or treat request was delivered in a deep voice accompanied by raucous laughter. I didn't get the joke so I quickly said I had nothing to give and closed the door.

Before I had sat down again, there was another knock at the door. I threw it open ready to send whoever it was packing and was greeted by a small child of about three or four looking up at me. The child had large brown eyes, made bigger and brighter by the porch light, set in the most angelic face I'd ever seen. He or she (I couldn't really tell under the floppy animal ears) was dressed in a white bunny rabbit costume, obviously left over from Easter, which contrasted with his chubby brown face. He was flanked by three slightly older children, who had put him at the front with good effect.

"Twick or tweet, lady?" the little voice lisped shyly.

"Trick or treat? You should be in bed at this time of night," I said, smiling down at him.

"She usually is," an adult female voice from behind the hedge further down the path said. "It's just a treat for tonight."

"Sorry, she's not in her witch's costume," one of the older children who was in her witch's costume with painted green face said. "She started to cry because she wanted to wear her bunny rabbit costume and Mummy had to sew the ear back on."

"I like my wabbit," the big eyed cherub said, grumpily pulling on one of her rabbit ears which looked as if it was in danger of coming off again.

"She wouldn't let Mummy paint her face either," another child added.

"'Cos the paint is itchy, stupid!" she of the heart-melting eyes replied. She turned and whacked the speaker with her plastic bag of goodies.

"Oww! Mum, she's doing it again!"

"Maisie," said the disembodied voice from beyond the hedge, "that's your final warning. If you don't behave you'll go right back home and stay with Daddy and the baby!"

The little rabbit folded her arms sulkily, clutching the offending weapon to her chest.

"Er... It's a lovely costume and you're probably right about the face paint," I said. "I'm sorry, though, I don't think I've got any treats. What trick are you going to play on me?"

The children all looked at each other blankly.

"We haven't thought of any tricks," the first witch said. "Everyone gives us sweets." I had to laugh.

"Okay, just wait there while I see what I can find."

Michael, my partner, who had been listening to the conversation, was shaking his head when I went back inside.

"Some people in this house are such hypocrites; so much for having nothing to do with Halloween," he said, smiling.

"I know, but babes, have you seen them... bless. I don't know what I'm going to give them."

"Well, there's that box of chocolates your sister gave you."

"Chocolates? Where are they?"

"You hid them from yourself on top of the kitchen cupboard... remember... so you wouldn't eat them all at once."

"Oh yes... I forgot."

"I think that was the idea."

"Well, I guess it worked then, didn't it?"

Friends of ours who had just moved into a new house had invited us to come and visit for the weekend and help them decorate.

Lolly's face lit up like a Christmas when I told her we were going away.

"You can come too," I said. "Many hands make light work. You can help Dad to paint."

"No thanks, Mum, you're all right," she answered. "You and Dad go and have a good time with the other wrinklies. I've got work after college on Friday and on Sunday and a psychology essay to finish."

Michael looked at me. I looked at my daughter suspiciously.

"Lolly... what are you planning?"

"Nothing," she answered putting on her most hurt and innocent face. "You just don't trust me do you?"

"No, it's not that," I answered guiltily. "I do trust you but..."

Michael looked at me again with raised eyebrows. I pulled a face at him.

"You can get one of your friends to come and stay with you... Krystal or Georgia, but you are not allowed to have a party. Do you hear me, Lolly?"

"Oh, Mum... as if..."

"Laura!"

"Yes... okay," she answered in that whining voice teenagers use which immediately makes your blood boil. Michael looked at her and cleared his throat.

"Sorry... but I won't... honest. I'll just have a couple of friends 'round to keep me company."

"Yes, that's okay but two or three, maximum."

That weekend, Michael and I went to Beth and Errol's and helped them with their decorating. There were quite a few of us there. It was like being in our twenties again. We stayed up all night, listening to some of Michael's old tunes from "back in the day", as he calls it: Mighty Diamonds, Winston Reedy and Third World.

I phoned Lolly a couple of times during the evening. The house sounded quiet and she assured me she was fine.

Meanwhile back at Beth and Errol's, the men cooked up a wicked pot of curry goat and rice with fried dumplings and plantain. The women put on rubber gloves, to save our nails, of course, and stripped the old wallpaper off the walls and sanded the paintwork. We ate, chatted, laughed, drank and had the whole house decorated by the time the postman arrived Saturday morning. Then we just all crashed out in sleeping bags wherever we could find space and slept until late Saturday afternoon.

Even queuing up for the two bathrooms before we went out to eat in the evening was funny. Someone suggested that, to save time, couples should go into the bathrooms together. Some bright spark thought a better idea was for the men to pick the women's names out of a hat to see who they got to go in with. A couple of the men thought it was a good idea. I think they were joking but we've got their cards marked. The women quickly made it clear we were having none of that.

Before we knew it, the weekend was over.

Having had a great time revisiting our youth with our friends, Michael and I arrived back at home Sunday morning feeling great.

"I'm sure that's Steven's bicycle," I said to Michael, pointing to the bike chained to the drainpipe at the side of the house. Steven is Lolly's boyfriend. I opened the front door apprehensively, not sure what I would find. The first thing that hit me was the smell... a lovely fresh perfume coming from the carpet which looked extremely clean.

"Lolly!" I called, but there was no answer. Then I remembered that she had gone to work. I put my weekend bag down in the hall gingerly. Michael and I looked at each other and he followed me, with an equally perplexed look, from room to room. There was no one about.

"Hmm, bwoy it look like we hav' fi goh weh more often," he said.

Every room was spotless. Our final stop was the kitchen. There had to be a burnt pot or a few plates and cups in the sink at least, but no. The sink was empty and sparkling clean, as was the cooker.

"I can't believe it," I said. "We've walked into the wrong house."

"Well, it looks like my baby girl has finally grown up. See, Kelly, I told you not to worry, when you wanted to come back last night. You really should start to trust her a bit more now, you know."

The telephone rang.

"Oh," said the surprised voice on the other end. "Hello, Aunty Kay. When... when did you get back?" Lolly's friend Krystal asked.

"A few minutes ago. Why?"

"Oh, nothing. Er... is... is Steven there?"

"No... why would Steven be here?" I asked suspiciously, remembering the bicycle outside.

"Er... no reason..."

"Krystal..."

"Well, you know I stayed there last night. I had to be at work for 8.30am and Lolly gave me a lift 'cos she started at 9.00am so we left Steven to tidy up."

"Lolly knows I don't like her driving into town when she's only just passed her driving test. Anyway, why was Steven here in the first place? And why would he need to tidy up?"

"After the party, er no... I mean... there were a few of us there last night... er... just me and Georgia. Not a party, though. Aunty Kay, please ask Steven if he found my earring. Got to go. Bye!"

The phone went dead before I could say anything else, but my attention had been caught by an old piece of wood sticking out from behind the coat stand. I pulled it out just as there was a knock at the door. It was Jill, our next door neighbour with her tired-looking baby on her hip.

"Hi, Kelly. How was your weekend?"

"It was really nice, Jill, thanks."

"Good. Is your Laura there?"

I shook my head.

"I'm really sorry if we spoilt her party last night. It wasn't us that called the police... honest. Mike at number three had his car broken into. I really don't think it was anything to do with those lads but maybe they shouldn't have sworn at the officer like that, then they wouldn't have been arrested. Normally we wouldn't mind the music at all but the bass kept waking the baby, and Pete had to go to work, first thing this morning – " I think the look on my face stopped her.

"Er... Kelly, are you all right? Do you want to come over and let me put the kettle on? I shook my head.

"You don't look so good."

Michael, who had heard it all, came to the door.

"It's all right, Jill, thanks," he said. "I'll come over and talk to you later, okay? Hello Baba. You look tired," he added, addressing the baby. The baby gave him a little tear-stained smile.

Jill looked at the piece of wood in my hand. I followed her gaze. Scrawled on the wood in white paint were the words I hadn't noticed until then 'Haunted House – This Way.' The words were followed by a big red arrow. "That was funny, eh?" Jill chuckled. "She put that at the end of the street and the spooky pumpkin lanterns in the garden were brilliant! Oh, I see the carpet cleaners did a good job." She started to walk back down the path as Michael was closing the door.

"What carpet cleaners?" I asked, opening the door again.

"The van came first thing this morning. The house smells gorgeous. Didn't know they worked on Sundays though. Your daughter is amazing," Jill added.

"Hmm, that's not the word I'd use for her!" Michael snorted. "I'm gonna bloody kill her!"

I rang Lolly's mobile phone but, of course, it was switched off and would have been even if she hadn't been in work.

"You need to talk to your daughter," Michael said.

"She's your daughter too! When did your baby girl suddenly become just my daughter?"

Michael took our weekend bags upstairs and immediately leaned over the banister and said in a loud whisper, "Kel, I think you'd better come upstairs."

Oh God, I thought, what next! Halfway up the stairs, I heard what sounded like a loud snore. Michael put his finger to his lips for me not to say anything. He was smiling. I hurried up the last few steps. I could hear the snores clearly now coming from the spare bedroom. Michael slowly opened the door to reveal Lolly's boyfriend, Steven, flat out on the bed, on his back, fast asleep. In one hand he clutched the top of the vacuum cleaner, in the other a dirty duster. Michael wanted to get his camera to take a photograph but I wouldn't let him. A picture of the last twenty-four hours events was beginning to unfold.

"Poor thing, leave him alone. He'll be embarrassed enough when he wakes up," I whispered as I closed the door again.

"The women in this family are heavy maintenance, man," Michael said. "See what you do to us. You've even worn poor little Steve out."

Downstairs in the kitchen I found one of the pumpkins with the scary carved faces and burnt-out candle in the dishwasher and another in the fridge.

By the time Lolly came home that evening, I had calmed down a little but it didn't last long.

"So your sister, Shari, knew you were having a party and said nothing?" I asked.

"Mum, it wasn't exactly a party, I keep telling you. I had to phone Shari when the fire alarm went off to ask her what to do because Krystal wanted to phone the fire brigade. I told her you don't need the fire brigade unless there is a real fire."

"What! Oh my God, it gets worse! So why did the fire alarm go off if there wasn't a fire?"

"Well... there was sort of a fire. The pizza caught fire, but don't worry. We put it out quickly." I looked at her with narrowed eyes.

"Where exactly was the fire?" I asked through clenched teeth?"

"Er... in the toaster. I managed to get a new one exactly the same and it was only a stain on the hall carpet... it came out. I thought it was burnt. I told Georgia you can't warm pizza on a toaster. Anyway, Shari paid for the carpet cleaner with her credit card. Krystal's sister only threw up because Uncle JJ scared her when he threw them all out. I told him she was drinking before she came and I don't know who walked the burnt pizza into the carpet - "

"Stop!" I shouted holding up my hand. "Breathe!" I had to put my hand up to stop her because she didn't even draw breath between sentences and she certainly wasn't giving me a chance to say anything.

"So let me get this right. My brother was also here?"

"Yes. Shari rang him after I rang her about the fire alarm. The grass!"

"Don't you call your sister names. At least she had the sense to get your uncle to come and sort you out."

"They were leaving anyway when he got here."

"Is this before or after the police came?"

"Oh... you know about that too, do you? Did Mike tell you? It was Jill next door, wasn't it? Lord, why is that woman so faas?"

"Just leave Jill out of this! Lolly, your friends shouldn't have been here in the first place! I am very disappointed!"

"I know, Mum. I know you said I couldn't have a party and I really didn't mean to but you said Krystal and Georgia could come 'round. We made dinner and then Tootsie came 'round."

Tiana aka Tootsie is my cousin Myra's daughter. I should have known she would be involved somehow.

"Well, Tootsie's friend, Asha, rang to see where she was 'cos she wanted to give her a new CD she'd just burned. So Asha came 'round with her sister and we were just listening to it. Then Asha's boyfriend rang to see what she was doing and she told him she was here and he could hear the music on the phone so he didn't believe her so he came 'round to check with some of his mates and –"

I held my hand up again to stop her. I had started to feel a headache coming on.

"Okay... okay... I think I'm beginning to get the picture but the sign 'Haunted House – This Way'?" I asked with raised eyebrows. This one should be good, I thought. And it was. My plans to ground her for the rest of her life and stop her pocket money for a month never got off the ground.

"Oh, the sign. Where did you find it?"

"Behind the coat stand where I assume Steven hid it... possibly for next year."

"Oh Mum, you're funny."

My face didn't feel like it was saying funny.

"And the lanterns, Lolly?"

"Ah... the... lanterns..."

"And Steven fast asleep upstairs? He's gone home now, by the way."

"Steve asleep upstairs? Never! I can explain... honest."

My face, which still wasn't saying funny, was now saying, I'm waiting... you'd better make this good, kid.

"Well... you know how you always say take care of the pennies and the pounds will take care of themselves?"

"Yes..." I answered slowly. I could hear the loud siren in my head. "Danger! Danger! You are about to fall into a Lolly trap."

"Well... I was walking past the Pound Shop, you know the new one on the high street next to ASDA, and didn't they have the biggest 75 percent off sale sign in the window."

"Lolly, what has this got to do with what happened here last night?" I asked patiently.

"I'm getting to that, Mum. Just chill... er, sorry. So, anyway, I had to go in and take a look at the sale, didn't I 'cos I know you would never pass a good bargain. They had that bath oil you wanted last time that they ran out of so I bought it for you. Fifty pence, Mum! Good eh?"

I shrugged. Bargain bath oil just wasn't going to cover it.

"Thank you but just get to the point, Laura, and stop trying to change the subject."

The fact that I had called her 'Laura' and not 'Lolly' I think gave her a clue as to how angry I was but she fought back using her best tactics. Lolly's face became a picture of hurt innocence that would have taken me in, if I hadn't fallen for it so many times before.

"Well," she continued when she realised the face hadn't worked. "Would you believe, right next to your bath oil were Halloween lanterns – not plastic , but real ones carved out of pumpkins and signs all at seventy-five percent off, Mum! If you think about it, it's really your fault for not letting us 'do' Halloween when we were kids.

I think I may have wanted to get it out of my system, all this time."

The headache had fully set in now.

"I knew, of course, what you said, that I couldn't have a party this time but I thought if I bought them now, I would save you some money for next year... if you change your mind... okay... not very likely now. I understand. But it was good thinking, eh, Mum? Eh?"

I sat down on a nearby chair and looked up just in time to see Michael's face disappear quickly from the other side of the glass panel in the door. It had that 'you're on your own with this one' look.

"So there you go, Mum. I didn't even have to wait for next year to save you money. 'Cos when the guys came round, I already had the lanterns and sign. Clever, eh? Give me a hug, Mum. You're not angry now, are you? I'm going to Steve's. See you later, Mum. Love you."

Michael, the coward, came in and found me, still sitting speechless on the chair. My daughter had pulled both a trick and treat caper, in one fell swoop.

"I'll put the kettle on and make you a cup of tea, love. Or maybe you need something a bit stronger, eh? We've still got a bit of rum left over from Christmas."

I nodded.

"Let's put it this way, Kelly, Lolly has chosen the right career. She'll make a brilliant psychologist. After all, she's been using her brain on us since she was born."

THE BATTLE OF THE BARBECUES

"If you were born here you are Black British, if you weren't born here, then you are Jamaican, Kelly," my aunt Beverley (Bliss) said emphatically. "Yu caan be both. No man, nut'n noh goh soh." It never failed to amuse me how my aunt could switch so seamlessly from perfect English one minute to patois the next to emphasise her point.

"But Aunty Bliss, I have a Jamaican passport and a British passport so that gives me dual nationality," I insisted, "but that's not the point I'm making, British immigration law is too complicated. It's the only country I know when even if you are born here, you are not automatically British."

"Unless yu a athlete," my mother chipped in. "Dem soh desperate now dat dem would an' draft in alien from Mars if him can run and call him British fi win a medal."

"Kelly right though yu know, Aunty Bliss. Mi read 'bout dat ina paper last week. Even if yu born here yu noh automatically British," my cousin Barbara (Babsie) said.

"Yu a read paper again, Babsie?" mum asked. "Yu noh learn from last time when we nearly noh goh a Jamaica because a yu?"

Babsie started to laugh. "Yu not funny yu know Aunty Mala."

We had been having this discussion that to the none Jamaican ear sounded more like an argument, about the quirks of the British immigration system and getting nowhere, for a good half hour.

On the first sunny Sunday we had had for a month, the family had gathered at my house for the return match in the 'battle of the barbecues' as my daughter Laura (Lolly) called it. So far, the women were winning one nil.

The women were sitting in my kitchen watching the men in their stripe aprons, bought specially for the occasion, with bags of barbecue bricketts and fire lighters, as they debated on the best way to light a barbecue and cook on it. They had their tea towels, paper plates, plastic forks and fire bucket full of water at the ready.

Amused, we watched them through the window strutting about, posturing in a testosterone haze. They were getting more hot and bothered by the minute as they took turns fanning and blowing in an attempt to get the coals burning properly.

"Well is my one deggeh deggeh Jamaican passport mi have from mi come 'ere Lord knows how many years ago. Mi noh wan' noh British one. Mek when dem wan' tek weh we likkle banana an' Blue Mountain coffee, like when dem did want di Arab dem oil, dem declare war pon Jamaica an' give mi gun fi goh kill mi own people dem. No sah."

"For heaven's sake, Aunty Bliss, that's not likely to happen," I said looking out of the window at the men who, with loud voices and animated gestures, were giving each other advice which no-one was taking.

"Hmm… what make yu so sure? Yu stay deh mek dem fool yu," Aunty Bliss answered.

"Yu taking a big risk there yu know, Aunty Bliss," Babsie said, "you've been here too long not to have taken out your British passport by now. What those men up to out there, Kelly? Any sign of any food cooking yet?"

"All I can see are clouds of smoke and nothing on the barbecue so far," I answered. "A definite case of too many cooks out there, I think."

"Never mind 'bout passport. If yu can run an' jump Bliss yu all right an' wid dem titty deh no-body going to ask you questions 'bout whether yu a man or woman like that poor South African athlete."

"Mi dear ma! A soh dem facey! All I can say is, duppy know who fi frighten. Bet dem would a never come wid dat to a Jamaican woman," Babsie said.

"After dem noh mad! Gender test? I would an' back off mi clothes right there an' show dem if mi a woman or not," Aunty Bliss laughed. "Kill dat deh argument dead! Dem wouldn't need noh rahtid test! Excuse me language Mala."

"Yu all right yu hear, Bliss, dem people ya would an' mek anybody cuss. Why nobody noh seem to notice how Britain and America a use up poor black people, especially Jamaicans, fi win medal fi dem," Mum said opening the window, "an' when di African dem beat us fair an' square all dem can come wid is foolishness. Oi you lot! Any chance we might get some food before mi turn skeleton!" she bellowed to the men.

"Is like during di war, yu know di story Uncle Zeb always a tell us, how we help dem win di war, then dem show us di door. Now dem only a use us fi win medal 'til dem find out why we can run so faas, then dem tek it an' gaan like seh a somet'ing new dem invent," Babsie said.

"Yes, that's exactly what I'm saying. Yu noh see how is only black people ina anyt'ing name sport these days, mum said. "An' little Jamaica always right in di middle a everyt'ing weh a gwaan."

"Well how yu fi win anyt'ing if yu belly boun' up wid Irish potato chips," Babsie laughed.

"But we noh have noh secret. Dem wan' giv dem white athlete deh some callaloo an' fresh fish. Yu t'ink Usain Bolt could an' run like dat if him maddah did bring him up on pot noodle and fish an' chips?" mum asked.

"No sah, me and Al watch that boy run in town in May in The Great Manchester Run, an' him look like him used to him fish tea and Irish moss," Aunty Bliss said. "A two hours Al mek mi stan' up wid him ina di rain yu know but it was worth it. When Usain come out an' smile the sun start to shine. Mi seh Usain leg dem move like dem set pon fast forward."

Just then my partner Michael, better known as Mixer, came to the window with a long barbecue fork with a wooden handle in his hand, red eyed and coughing with ashes in his hair. Uncle Al, wearing a red green and gold bandana under his white chef's hat, had taken over from him stoking the coals on the barbecue.

A scream from Uncle Al made me look up just in time to see him box his chef's hat off the barbecue with his giant fork. It had fallen off his head and immediately burst into flames. The blazing hat flew into the air, narrowly missing Ferdie who had to duck. Unfortunately, Ferdie who had been balancing in a garden chair on two legs, fell heavily onto the grass, with the chair on top of him.

With great presence of mind, Richie, Ferdie and Babsie's son grabbed the fire bucket of water and threw it in the direction of the hat but half of the water landed on Ferdie. Richie stood with the empty bucket in his hand, trying not to laugh.

"Sorry Dad," he said.

Ferdie picked himself up and stomped up to Uncle Al.

"Gimme di blouse an' skirt fork! A kill yu a try fi kill mi?"

"Ah sorry man, ah sorry," was all Uncle Al could say sheepishly. "Weh yu did wan' mi fi do?"

Michael shook his head as the women who had ran to the window at the sound of the commotion, fell about laughing.

"You lot have a warped sense of humour, do you know that?" he said. "Man nearly get bun up an' unnuh a laugh? Pass me the chicken, Kelly."

After two hours, they got the coals glowing enough to put the chicken on the grill. The previous night with mum's ominous warning of food poisoning ringing in our ears, Michael had singed and scrubbed the chicken pieces meticulously with lime before seasoning them.

"Mi noh wan' end up in the Infirmary wid bad belly like Aunt Mary before har wedding," mum said.

"Do you think we should tell them we've cooked already?" Babsie asked.

"No man, leave dem let dem strut up an' down like peacock an' mek noise out there. Dem a enjoy demself. When dem finish cook dem salmonella food, we'll give dem some real dinner," Mum chuckled.

It might have sounded cruel but we were getting our own back. Why do men always have to turn everything into a competition? Or is that just the men in our family?

It had all started a couple of months before when we had one of our rare sunny days in England and even more rare in Manchester. We decided to do something different to make the most of the sunshine. My daughter Laura (Lolly) suggested a barbecue. She has these brilliant flashes of inspiration from time to time.

Michael, who was having one of his few Sundays at home, thought it was a good idea too. He is a builder and with the recession hitting the building trade hard, he had to take whatever work he could get, often working weekends out of town.

At the local supermarket, Lolly and I bumped into my cousin Babsie and her family in the home and garden section, looking at barbecues.

We joined the long line of people with barbecues, meat and an assortment of plastic utensils in their shopping trollies who had obviously had the same idea.

"Why are you both buying barbecues?" Lolly asked. "Why don't you all come to our house and have one barbi?"

It made perfect sense but it would have been nice if she had asked me first. From past experience, I knew I needed to prepare mentally for these family events and my nerves had taken a battering over the years. I still hadn't fully recovered from the trip to London for my Aunt Dar's funeral with the female members of the clan in the eight-seater people carrier.

I had been newly diagnosed with high blood pressure and my doctor had suggested that I should avoid stressful situations. Yeah right... she didn't have to live with my eccentric family.

Arriving back at our house, as punishment, I had given Lolly the task of phoning everyone to tell them to bring some food or a drink or both. I forgot the telephone was Lolly's favourite toy so this job took a little longer than expected. In fact, the first family members had arrived before Lolly finished her calls. I think she got in a few sneaky calls to her friends while she was there.

Live cricket had been on the television, and unable to get the men away from it, the women had taken charge of the barbecue. The men had berated us mercilessly for the length of time it took us to get the coals going and for the fact that we pre-cooked all the meat in the oven before putting it on the barbecue. It had all been edible and actually very tasty but they reckoned we made work for ourselves and they could have done it much better. So we had challenged them to go ahead. Once the gauntlet was thrown down, the men decided to rise to the challenge. That was why we women were now in the kitchen watching and laughing at them.

Michael had decided that they weren't going to have any old shop bought barbecue, he would build his own. He spent several evenings like an excited little boy, with Uncle Al and Ferdie, measuring, making drawings as if he was redesigning Buckingham Palace itself and making one almighty mess in the back garden with bricks and cement.

"Michael!" I shouted as a cloud of dust rose in the air and I ran out to rescue my white clothes from the washing line. He sat back on his heels looking at me with a smile.

Uncle Al looked at him. "Mixer, a wha' sweet yu soh?" he asked. Michael just shook his head and laughed. He beckoned for me to come closer and cupping his hands whispered in my ear,

"Run 'cross the garden again let me see noh Kelly."

"What?" I asked puzzled. I think Uncle Al and Ferdie must have heard what he said or just caught on quicker than I did because they had their heads down with very suspicious looking smiles.

"Bwoy yu bottom ina dem jeans is a sight for sore eyes," Michael said.

I was so embarrassed I didn't know what to say. Uncle Al and Ferdie were chuckling now.

"Kelly stop distracting Mixer. It won't work," Uncle Al said. "Stay strong, son. No time fi dat now, just keep yu eye on di job. We have to show these women what a real barbecue is."

"Unnuh too idle," I said but I couldn't keep the smile off my face as I pulled my blouse down over my bottom and walked back into the house.

The bespoke barbecue was a sight to behold and Michael who missed no chance to show it off got several orders to build similar ones for our neighbours and their friends.

Now the great day had arrived. The cat from across the road which had been sitting on the fence with two others watching the proceedings keenly, suddenly jumped down. It made a run for the bowl with the chicken pieces when it thought Michael wasn't looking. In its eagerness, the cat knocked the entire bowl and its contents onto the grass.

As if it had been planned, the two other cats and another that I hadn't seen hiding in the hedge, darted forward and seized chicken pieces. They scurried away, scrambling up the fence accompanied by curses, shouts of outrage and Ferdie's half drunk can of lager.

Swearing under his breath, Michael picked the remaining chicken pieces up and brought them into the kitchen.

"Before you say anything, mi not throwing dem 'way and if one a unnuh laugh, unnuh dead," he said, waving a chicken leg threateningly at us.

"Mi!" Aunty Bliss said. "A noh unnuh mi a laugh after, a Kelly jus' tell mi joke."

I nodded vigorously putting on my most innocent face. After all my partner's pride was hanging in tatters and it's on these occasions that a woman has to support her man.

Michael kissed his teeth as he picked bits of grass off the chicken.

"Blasted puss! If a lick him yu see. Yu jus' watch mi an' him. A gwaan mek a sling shot just fi him." He carefully washed and seasoned the chicken again.

He turned to us. "Unnuh gwaan laugh yu si, unnuh a goh laugh pon di other side a unnuh face when we present you with this gourmet feast."

"Hmm… unnuh can eat my share a di gourmet feast if unnuh want," mum said. "Mi definitely nah eat none a dat deh puss left chicken. Mi noh ready fi move ina fi mi plot a Southern Cemetery yet."

Babsie let the side down first and the rest of us followed, holding on to each other with the laughter bursting out until tears ran down our faces. I laughed until my stomach started to hurt.

"Unnuh a idiot," Michael said as he kissed his teeth and went out again with his chicken.

A few minutes later, the cat having devoured his ill-gotten spoils, jumped up onto the fence again, looking eagerly to see if there was anymore. The stone Uncle Al threw at it hit the fence with a loud bang and the poor cat nearly fell off the fence as it scooted off in fear of its life.

"Yu facey brute yu! Come back if yu t'ink yu bad," Uncle Al shouted.

Our next door neighbour, Pete's head appeared over the hedge. I had seen him peeping through the hedge at the sound of the men's antics, earlier. With the bang, curiosity had got the better of him.

I knew that Jill his wife, had gone shopping leaving him with strict instructions to mow the lawn and trim the hedge because I and all the other neighbours had heard her shouting at him that morning before she slammed her car door and drove off.

"Get it done, Pete, or I'm warning you, you'll be sleeping out there in a tent tonight!"

"All right, love. I will, honest."

"You'd better! I lost the baby in the bloody grass yesterday and I've not seen the dog for days!"

She was exaggerating of course… I think, but their garden was looking more like a jungle every day. You know what they say about the plumber always having a leak in his house? Well Pete was a landscape gardener.

"Hey, Mixer!" I heard him shout.

"Hi Pete," Michael answered. "What's up?"

"The missus has left me to do the garden but I'm fed up. You got room for one more over there? I've got beer."

"Yeah, sure mate. Just come round."

Pete's head disappeared and I saw Ferdie kiss his teeth.

Minutes later Pete appeared at the front door with a package of sausages, a package of beef burgers and a six pack of lager.

"Afternoon ladies," he said. "Hi Babsie."

"Hello Pete. What do you think about Britain drafting in all these black athletes to represent them?" mum asked, as he walked through the kitchen.

"Well, they're British Mrs M. Most of them were born and bred here so why not. It's their country. Besides, we wouldn't win a bloody thing otherwise would we? Pardon the language ladies." Pete continued through into the garden.

I had to smile. I had watched him from my bedroom window after Jill left. Like Indianna Jones, whistling, he had battled his way through the knee-high grass to the garden shed. He had got the lawn mower, the hedge trimmer and the step ladder out but that was as far as he had got after he found the deck chair. Still whistling, he had gone back into the house for his newspaper and a can of lager and settled himself under the apple tree. An hour later he was still there, fast asleep.

Pete's skin was usually white but he had turned an interesting shade of pink because he had stayed in the sun too long. A lot of white folk when they discover they have black neighbours don't like it due either to the negative stereotypes they have of black people or plain racism; not Peter or his wife Jillian who greeted us when we moved in by bringing us a large apple pie. It quickly became obvious on meeting Pete that before meeting Michael he had been a black man in waiting.

When Pete found out Michael was a disc jockey in his spare time and had all the old Bob Marley songs, I think he thought

Christmas and his birthday had come at once. He and Michael became friends immediately and he often accompanied Michael when he played at gigs at the West Indian Community Centre.

Reggae music wasn't all Pete loved, he had a passion for Jamaican food, jerk chicken and rice 'n' peas in particular, which Michael had taught him to cook. He had in turn taught Michael to make shepherd's pie and bread and butter pudding.

We could always tell when he and Jill had had an argument because he would play Bob Marley 'No Woman Noh Cry' at full volume again and again. Pete got on with everyone except Ferdie who kept a close eye on him because although he never said or did anything improper, it was pretty obvious that he fancied Babsie.

As often happens with the British weather, the day of the rematch barbecue started off hot and sunny. By mid afternoon, the sky had clouded over and shortly after Pete came over, the heavens opened with a massive downpour. We actually felt sorry for the men as they rescued what they could and ran inside.

"Admit it, Al," Aunty Bliss said, "we win! At least you got to eat the food we cooked. That lot isn't safe to eat."

She pointed at the tray Uncle Al was carrying with an assortment of half cooked chicken, lamb chops, burgers and sausages. As for the corn, they were barely recognisable as corn.

"Wha'appen to yu, a bit of butter, black pepper or burnt chef's hat on this and it'll be fine won't it, Al?" Michael said picking up a piece of corn off the tray.

"I just wanted Kelly to run out in her jeans and help us carry everything in," he added, winking at me. Everyone except Uncle Al and Ferdie gave him a puzzled look.

"A tell yu, we win!" Aunty Bliss said again. "Hands down, Al."

"Yu noh win a t'ing," Uncle Al said. "Rain stop play, man. Act of God don't count. We want a rematch next week."

"Act of God all right," mum said. "God wash 'way unnuh burnt offering. Well it's just as well while you were out there having fun, we cook dinner. Now all of you stop cluttering up the kitchen. Go an' wash up an' come eat."

I think the men were relieved that they hadn't been forced because of pride to eat the charred food they had prepared that even the cats had lost interest in.

"Thank goodness for the rain," Pete chuckled. "At least now I have an excuse for not doing the garden and Jill can't make me sleep outside."

UNCLE ZEB'S WEDDING

My Great Uncle Zeb, my mother's uncle, got married at 83. Uncle Zeb and Aunt Mary had been together for sixty-four years. They have seven children, twenty-six grandchildren, ten great grand children and six great great grandchildren who filled the front pews of the local Seventh Day Adventist church.

Aunt Mary and Uncle Zeb could have graced the front cover of any high society magazine. Aunt Mary looked like a delicate brown fairy queen as her eldest son, Jacob (Jake), led her down the aisle. She was dressed in layers of soft white silk and lace with a lace veil dotted with tiny pearls. Her snow-white hair peeped out from under her veil in baby curls. Leaning on his walking stick, Uncle Zeb stood proudly next to his best man, Uncle Al, at the altar. He was dressed in a cream Armani suit, a present from Little Levi, one of his grandchildren. His walking stick, another present, was polished oak with a golden snake's head.

It came as quite a shock, and a source of great amusement, to most of the family, when Uncle Zeb announced that he had proposed to Aunt Mary and she had accepted. Most of the family, including all their children, thought they were already married.

"We intended to," Uncle Zeb said, in the quiet way he had of speaking, "when we first got together during the Second World War, but Mary wanted a big church wedding so we decided to save up for it."

The first babies had arrived apparently quite close together. The right time or enough money had just not come along for a wedding. As the years had gone by and everyone assumed they were married,

Uncle Zeb and Aunt Mary had been too embarrassed to say otherwise. I wondered how no-one, especially their children, had ever questioned the lack of wedding photographs.

Jake didn't take it well. In fact, he was rushed to the local hospital with a suspected heart attack, which turned out to be indigestion. He still swears that was what brought on his high blood pressure, not the fact, as Aunty Bliss pointed out in her own unique style, that he happened to be four stones overweight. I suppose to discover at 61 that your parents had never married would be difficult enough for anyone. Jake was an upstanding pillar of the community with the position of head deacon in the church and deputy secretary on the West Indian Community Centre management committee and had a reputation to uphold.

Jake was finally convinced after several visits to his doctor, that he really hadn't suffered a heart attack and was not about to die. He wanted just to take his parents off for a quiet registry office wedding, preferably out of town, and bring them home again with not a word said to anyone.

Little Levi, Jake's eldest son, didn't help the situation when he half jokingly suggested that Uncle Zeb and Aunt Mary should run away across the border to Gretna Green, like couples did in the past when their parents disapproved of them marrying.

"The problem is that in this case, it isn't the parents who don't approve of the wedding, it's the children!" Uncle Zeb pointed out crossly. "We would elope, just to teach Jake a lesson, but my old rheumatic knees and Mama's bad back wouldn't allow us to run anywhere and definitely not as far as across the Scottish border."

"Never mind Gramps," Little Levi said, "Just give Dad time, he'll come round."

"Yu gran' maddah wait over half a century for a big white wedding and that's exactly what she is going to have," Uncle Zeb said emphatically.

For months Uncle Zeb's wedding was a heated topic of conversation which really highlighted for me the differences in the generations. All the family under thirty thought it was hilarious and that Uncle Zeb and Aunt Mary should have the biggest wedding ever.

The thirty-somethings thought it was mildly amusing and a little embarrassing but not such a big deal. The non-Christian forty-somethings didn't care one way or the other and the Christian forty-somethings and upwards, led by Jake, thought it was shameful and a disgrace on the family which would tarnish our good name for generations.

"Hmm!" my Aunty Bliss remarked. "Jake, a foolishness yu a gwaan wid man. We already have so many skeletons in this family anyway, who's going to notice or care about a little extra tarnish."

"It's all right for you Bliss; they're not your parents! I'll never be able to hold my head up anywhere respectable again," Jake complained bitterly.

"For heaven's sake Jacob behave yuself," my mother said impatiently ."This is not about you. Yu know how many black people live together happily – well maybe some not soh happily - but dem live all di same, for years without getting married?"

"Yes, an' di minute dem get married dem husband run off wid someone half dem age," Cousin Myra whose husband had done just that added.

"Leave that now Myra," Mum said. "Where Zeb going to run to at his age, except ina him grave. Now Jake, I know how you feel but a lot of time, it's people's kids who pay for their wedding when they get old."

Jake was having a good swim in a sea of self-pity and was not to be convinced so easily.

Pastor Franklin, newly ordained minister and member of the thirty-somethings, admitted 'off the record' that it was the best laugh he'd had for a long time. I think Jake had been hoping Pastor Franklin would be outraged and refuse to marry Uncle Zeb and Aunt Mary, so he could pursue his plans for a quiet registry office wedding out of town. In fact, to Jake's disappointment, Pastor

Franklin announced to everyone that Uncle Zeb and Aunt Mary were two of his best evangelists and tithe paying church members and he would be honoured to marry them.

So another family skeleton came out of the closet for fresh air. Two of the oldest members of our family, fine upstanding members of the church, had been living in sin for longer than most of the rest of the family had been alive. Life's a funny thing.

Well at least Uncle Zeb's revelation answered the intriguing question of why he and Aunt Mary never took communion and had over the years refused to accept every church post that had been offered to them although they worked tirelessly behind the scenes.

The difference of opinion over Uncle Zeb's wedding, continued until the night Aunt Mary took ill and had to be rushed to the Accident and Emergency Department at the Royal Infirmary. I don't know why most crisis seems to start in the middle of the night. The persistent ringing of the telephone awakened me. Still asleep, I mumbled for Michael my partner to answer it before I remembered that he was working away in London for the week. It was Jake. The panic in his voice brought me wide-awake immediately.

"You've got to come, Kelly. Mama sick bad and we can't persuade her to go to hospital. She keeps asking for you."

I scribbled a note to my sleeping teenage daughter, Laura, and drove the couple of miles along streets deserted apart from a couple of foraging foxes, to Uncle Zeb's house.

Aunt Mary didn't look good at all. She was lying on her bed rubbing her stomach and moaning, her fine baby hair pasted to her head with perspiration. Uncle Zeb and Jake looked very concerned. Aunt Mary opened her eyes when she heard my voice.

"Kelly, come say a prayer for me. Pain a lick mi bad. All day mi a try fi dust it out but mi belly feel like Satan himself in there."

She looked at Uncle Zeb and whispered, "I don't think I'm going to make it this time, Kelly."

After asking her a few questions, I agreed with Jake that we needed to get her to hospital quickly. Aunt Mary began to cry.

"No Kelly, mi already tell Jake mi caan goh a hospital. Dem a goh kill mi wid di marsa." I looked at Jake, puzzled.

"Marsa?" I mouthed to him.

"MRSA, Kelly," Jake whispered. "You know, that new super bug that everyone in hospital keeps catching."

"No need to whisper Jake. I know it's MRSA. I'm old not stupid. Kelly is jus' mi an' Zeb call it that because it's easier for the old brain to say."

"Don't get upset, Aunt Mary. I understand and Jake wasn't saying you're stupid," I said gently.

"Mi frighten 'cos only this week mi read in the paper how one woman die in the Infirmary and she only goh in for dem fi cut har in-growing toenail," Aunt Mary said.

"Aunt Mary, you know the papers always make things out to be worse than they are. I'll come with you and make sure no-one touches you unless they wash their hands."

"T'ank yu, Kelly, but doctor and nurse please demself. Yu caan tell dem what to do. If I'm going to die I want to stay in my own home."

Another ten minutes of vomiting and worsening stomach pains and Aunt Mary agreed to let Jake drive her to the Accident and Emergency Department. I think it was seeing how worried Uncle Zeb was that finally swung it. She refused to let us call an ambulance as she said she didn't want to give the neighbours any gossip.

As we sat waiting anxiously while the doctor examined Aunt Mary and she was put on a drip because she was so dehydrated, Uncle Zeb and Jake paced the room anxiously.

"Did I ever tell you how we met, Kelly?" Uncle Zeb asked. He had, numerous times but I didn't feel this was a good time to point that out.

"Why don't you tell me again, Uncle," I encouraged.

"A lot of people these days don't know that many people from the West Indies fought in the Second World War."

"Yes, I know Uncle."

"Me and your Aunty Mary were among the first from Jamaica to volunteer. I was really too young for the air force but I lied about my age when I went to the recruiting office."

"Really? You came all the way from Jamaica to fight in the war?"

"Oh yes," Uncle Zeb sat on the chair beside me. "A lot of us did; we thought it was our duty. England was the Mother Country you see. It wasn't as it is now... people welcomed us and treated us well, especially the English ladies. They loved us coloured boys but I wasn't interested in any of them. It was after the war the problems started... when they didn't need us anymore. They just wanted us to go away quietly." He gave a little chuckle.

"Yu ever see a Jamaican do anyt'ing quietly, Kelly?"

"No Uncle, your right," I smiled.

"Your Aunt Mary and I met at a garden party in 1943."

Jake had sat down and was listening now.

"You never told me that, Papa," he said.

"Yes, it was given in honour of the West Indian ATS... the Auxiliary Territorial Service. Oh yu maddah was a little brown skin beauty, Jacob... I couldn't take my eyes off her... couldn't believe someone could have a waist so small. Yu remember that reggae song that was popular some years back, Kelly... Miss Wire Waist? That was my Mary. I had to laugh every time I heard that song." Uncle Zeb's old eyes took on a far away look.

"I came to England in 1942 to train as a pilot and Mary was in the Women's Auxiliary Air Force. We were here long before that ship, the Empire Windrush, brought West Indians here in 1948. I served with 139 Jamaica Squadron. Did I ever tell you about the time I met the Right Honourable Oliver Stanley?"

"Yes Uncle."

"Well he was the Secretary of State for the Colonies at the time yu know?"

"Yes Uncle."

We were at the hospital until morning when they finally found Aunt Mary a bed so she could be admitted. She stayed in for a couple of days without contracting MRSA, to her relief. She refused to eat the hospital "taste bad food", as she called it. We had to take all her meals in and a couple of litres of disinfectant to wash everything before she would touch it.

It turned out Aunt Mary just had a bad bout of food poisoning from a tin of ackee she had found in the back of her cupboard. Uncle Zeb had wisely refused to eat any of it.

"I don't know what the fuss is all about," Aunt Mary said. "I only had it for two years. We never threw anything away during the war. Me an' Zeb once ate a tin of beef stew we'd had for three years." Uncle Zeb swallowed hard. He had obviously been unaware of the age of his beef stew dinner.

"What! Mary, yu give mi three year old stew fi eat? Mi noh know if mi fi marry yu now. Yu a try fi kill mi!"

"Shut up, man! Yu eat five year old corn beef an' yu noh know. It noh do yu a t'ing. Yu a 83! If mi did want fi kill yu, yu would an dead wid yu teet' skin long time."

Uncle Zeb's face was a picture as he was completely lost for words to answer.

Aunt Mary's trip to hospital did the trick though because it gave Jake such a fright. He decided that if Aunt Mary wanted a white wedding with all the trimmings, he would spare no expense to make sure she got it and be damned with what people thought.

So that was how we came to be planning the biggest wedding in the history of our family with relatives coming from the five continents of the world and a few who looked weird enough to have come from a bit further than that, my mother remarked.

It was at the church that we found out that Uncle Zeb is named after the tribes of Israel – all twelve of them. Aunty Mary has one name. She said that when she asked her parents why, her father had said that he had never read anywhere in the Bible about Mary having another name. If it was good enough for the mother of Jesus, it was good enough for his little baby girl.

Pastor Franklin said, "Do you Zebulun, Reuben, Simeon... Levi ..." he paused, looking perplexed. There was a chorus of "Amen!" and a few claps. Someone shouted,

"Yes, thank you Jesus! Good godly names!"

A couple of people shouted "Amen!"

Pastor Franklin scratched his head and continued. "...Judah, Dan, Naphtali... er... Gad..." he paused again and looked at Uncle Zeb who just smiled in his sparkling new false teeth. His baldhead and face shone with the Vaseline Aunt Mary had rubbed on him. She had left a little blob of Vaseline on his ear but no-one had noticed earlier and it was too late to do anything about it now. I made a mental note to rub some of the Vaseline off him with a tissue before the photographs so his head wouldn't shine too much.

Everyone was smiling now and looking at each other with questioning, raised eyebrows. Pastor Franklin cleared his throat with a smile and continued. "... Asher, Issachar, Joseph, Benjamin Stevens."

Someone at the back of the church, I think it was Cousin Myra, shouted,

"Hallelujah! Bless him, Lord!"

Aunty Bliss shouted, "Amen!" and began to applaud. Everyone else began to applaud too. Uncle Zeb was beaming from ear to ear. His new dentures gleamed in the light as Aunt Mary looked up at him adoringly.

At this point, Angie, Jakes sister who now lives in America, got into the spirit. She threw her hands in the air and started speaking in tongues in an American accent. My mother kissed her teeth loudly.

"Mum," I hissed, "behave!"

"Spirit mi foot bottom," mum whispered loudly. "She jus' a show off herself. A soh she stay from she little."

I think Angie must have heard mum because the spirit suddenly took flight and left her. Angie straightened her hat, which had almost fallen off her head and gave my mum a dirty look.

Pastor Franklin who had stood quietly with his head bowed looked at them both pointedly and loudly said, "Amen," before he continued the service.

"…take this woman Mary, to be your lawful wedded wife?"

"I most certainly do," Uncle Zeb answered.

Pastor Franklin leaned forward and whispered something to Uncle Zeb and Aunt Mary. They both nodded.

"Do you, Mary Leason take this man, Zeb Stevens –".

"Yeah man! Nice one Pastor! Short an' sweet!" someone at the back shouted.

There was a cheer and another round of applause.

"Please ladies and gentlemen, let us remember where we are," Pastor Franklin said, pointing to the huge sign above his head which said in gold lettering "…Reverence My Sanctuary."

"Let us continue… Do you Mary Leason take this man, Zebulun Stevens to be your lawful wedded husband?"

"Yes siree!" Aunt Mary shouted.

Pastor cleared his throat and leaned forward. "Er… Just 'I do' will do Sister Stevens…er Leason," he whispered.

"Sorry Pastor, I do," Aunt Mary said. "I mean I'm not sorry I do. I just do. It's a bit late now if I don't, eh Pastor? Who else a goh have him?"

The entire church burst out laughing and clapping. Even Pastor Franklin started to laugh. Uncle Zeb just squeezed Aunt Mary's hand and smiled. When it got to his part, he seemed to be struggling with his new dentures, so he discreetly turned to the side, quickly slipped them out into his handkerchief and in a loud, clear voice took his vows. When he had finished, he put them back in again.

We all agreed later that it was the most entertaining wedding ceremony we had ever witnessed. I won't even begin to tell you about the wedding reception but you should know my family by now so you can just use your imagination.

For their honeymoon we clubbed together and sent Uncle Zeb and Aunt Mary on a cruise around the West Indies. At the time some of us were a little concerned that a cruise might be too strenuous for them at their age but that was two years ago. They both got the bug... not MRSA but the travelling bug and rang Jake from the Bahamas two months after they left, telling him to put their house up for rent.

The last postcard Jake got with a photograph of Aunty Mary in a grass hula hula skirt and Uncle Zeb in a colourful shirt and Panama hat, was from Hawaii. It said... Married life is great. Missing everyone but not enough to come back any time soon...

Love Mama and Papa. XXX

THE DAY TRIP

We were up at 7.00am, as soon as the alarm went off. Well, I was up anyway. Michael sat on the bed, yawning and scratching sleepily as I threw the curtains back.

"Kelly man," Michael said shielding his eyes from the sunlight. "Wha'appen to yu! Oh man… why did I let you talk me into this? Do we have to go?"

"Yes," I said pulling the duvet out from underneath him as I made the bed. "Get a move on babes. You'll enjoy it; better than staying at home and it looks like it's going to be a nice day."

"Hmm… don't let the sunshine fool yu, it'll be raining in a minute," he grumbled.

"That's why I've packed our umbrellas. Come on."

Laura (Lolly) my daughter and Michael hadn't been too keen when I had first suggested going on the day trip with the members of Cousin Myra's church. I had learnt well over the years from Lolly how to use subtle psychology on my family to get them round to my way of thinking. I don't know where Michael got the idea from that Lolly got it from me.

I don't keep 'black people time' so with our bag of fried chicken, potato salad and buttered hard dough bread rolls, we were outside the church next to Trinity High School at 8.20am sharp – a whole ten minutes before the time my cousin Babsie said we had to be there.

The old church looked derelict and was dark and locked up, tight. I looked up and down the street but there was not a blessed soul in sight and no coach, just a stray dog, head down, idly sniffing every lamp-post it passed and leaving the occasional deposit of urine.

"That's funny… where is everybody?" I asked.

"Still ina dem bed if dem have any sense," Michael answered grumpily, yawning again and snuggling down into his coat. "Don't like the look of round here, Kel. Mi noh wan' leave mi baby park here all day yu noh. We might come back an' find mi new tyre dem gaan."

"Are you sure you've got the right day, Mum?" Lolly asked.

I was beginning to wonder myself. I'd never been to Myra's church before and after ten minutes, we were beginning to think we must be in the wrong place so we drove around to the other side of the school to see if there was another church, but there wasn't. I rang Cousin Babsie.

"Why are you still at home?" I asked Babsie's husband, Ferdie, who answered the phone as grumpily as Michael. He handed the phone to Babsie without a word.

"Oh Lord!" Babsie cried. "Yu there already? Ferdie get up man! Goh get di bag a food! If Richie gaan back to bed a gwaan lick him yu si."

"Aren't we supposed to be here for 8.30am? Why is no-one else here?" I asked.

"Kelly yu too English man. Don't yu know black people don' goh anywhere on time? I only said I might get there for 8.30am to get a space in the church car park. Don' worry we're leaving now – be there in a minute. Richie!"

Lolly sat grouchily with her arms folded in the back of the car. Michael's face reflected hers perfectly. Talk about chip not flying far from the block.

"Mum, do you have to be so cheerful so early in the morning?" Lolly asked pulling her coat over her head as I started singing along to the radio.

The day had started bright and sunny but with a chilly breeze. We had dressed in several layers for all weathers: starting with sleeveless vests, t-shirts, sweat shirts and finally waterproof coats with umbrellas for back up. Everyone had two kinds of footwear: sandals and trainers... just in case.

Eventually Babsie arrived and we rang Cousin Myra when still no-one else had arrived. It turned out we were at the church beside the wrong school. When we finally arrived at the right church, the situation looked a bit more hopeful. The church was open and there were a few people milling about, some with bigger food bags than ours which was a relief, although there was still no coach in sight.

"8.30am?" Cousin My laughed. "A who tell yu dat? Mi tell Babsie, and everyone else, 9.30am and that's only because mi know she always late fi everyt'ing. The coach nah leave 'til 10.00am."

Michael rolled his eyes with a groan, stuffed his hands into his pockets and headed back for the car followed by Lolly but I ignore them and went to socialise with the other early birds.

The coach duly arrived. It was a luxury 52 seater, one of the new ones with front wing mirrors like a charging bull's horns. Michael and his grumpy daughter settled themselves on the back seat. Plugged into their iPods, they were both nodding their heads to music thirty years apart. At 9.45am the coach was still half empty. At 9.55am cars started to appear from no-where, screeching to a halt and blocking the road with people shouting, laughing and blowing their horns as they greeted each other.

Everyone eventually boarded with their food bags. For once my mother didn't look out of place with her hold all and carrier bags of food. The air in the coach began to smell of fried chicken and Michael started rooting about in our bag.

"Leave the chicken alone, we haven't even left," I said, moving the bag away from him.

"But I didn't have any breakfast, Kelly. I'm starving man; just one little chicken leg."

"No, have some fruit," I said giving him a banana.

"Yu are a cruel woman, yu know that? Yu t'ink fruit can full big man belly."

We prayed and the coach was manoeuvring its way out of the

little street, when a battered old people carrier came racing around the corner and screeched to a halt in front of it, forcing the driver to brake sharply. There were a few gasps.

"Lord bless us an' save us!" Cousin Myra shouted. "A which idiot dat sah?" My leaned across the aisle and peered out of the window. "Oh Blessed Lord… a Pastor; mi noh figet 'bout dem. Noh tell him seh mi call him idiot yu noh but him should an' hav more sense dan dat."

A large woman, who I assumed was the pastor's wife, jumped out of the car more energetically than her size would imply, waving frantically as she grabbed bags. Four children like little chicks jumped out of the car and ran for the coach. The pastor expertly reversed into his space in the church car park and ran onto the coach too.

"Good morning Mr Coach Driver; my apologies. Good morning… good morning good people," the pastor said. "Apologies… apologies to one and all for being late; we're here now so let's be off. Praise the Lord!"

As the coach was about to pull away again, we heard a shout,

"Wait fi mi! Unnuh wait fi mi!" An elderly woman with a small child, came hurrying down the road, waving her umbrella. The little boy was laughing and dancing about as small children do when they get over excited and don't know what to do with themselves.

"Chile a wha wrong wid yu? Behave yuself an' goh sidung! T'ank yu dahling," she said to the coach driver. "God bless yu."

"Praise the Lord, Sister," the pastor said.

"Sister Joseph, I did say 9.30am yu know," Cousin My said.

"Ah sorry Sister My but di pickney here maddah jus' bring him."

"Ah right Sister Jo; glad yu could make it. Take yu seat quickly," Cousin My said. "Driver, let us go." Cousin My leaned close to the driver's ear,

"Ignore anybody else yu see coming an' just drive," she whispered.

Cousin My's pastor introduced himself as Pastor Smilie. The

Smilies reminded me of the nursery rhyme 'Jack Sprat'. You know the one…. "Jack Sprat could eat no fat, his wife could eat no lean." Pastor Smilie was stick thin with a full mouth of gleaming white teeth that looked like he was wearing them for someone else because they were too much for his little face. Sister Smilie was the complete opposite – she was one of those women who look like they've got someone else's share of bottom and breasts along with their own. She looked half Chinese with a pretty round face and little eyes that disappeared when she laughed.

The Smilies were Smilie by name and nature and were good adverts for religion. Every other word out of their mouths was "praise the Lord." Their two boys were miniature Pastor smilies and the two girls were exact copies of Sister Smilie.

One of Cousin My's church sisters who had just come back from the Jamaica Gospel Festival, had a CD of Jabez one of the singers. As we joined the bank holiday traffic on the M56 motorway, Sis Smilie got out her tambourine. The whole coach started to rock as we clapped and sang at the top of our voices to 'Mi Seh Mi Know Seh Mi Bless.' The coach driver was singing louder than everyone else although I don't think he understood a word of what he was singing. The other motorists gave us some curious looks but we didn't care. Some of them blew their horns and waved at us as they passed.

"Driver we're glad you're singing along but don't start clapping whatever you do," my mother shouted. "Just keep your hands on the wheel!"

"Yu maddah start early," Michael remarked, smiling.

Half an hour into the journey, stuck in heavy traffic on the M56, Cousin Myra's mobile phone rang. It was someone who had just turned up at the church wanting to know why the coach wasn't still there.

"'Bout mi fi ask di driver fi come back fi har. Bwoy some people facey yu si," Cousin My said kissing her teeth. "That's what's wrong with our people why we can't get anywhere yu know."

"Never mind My. We left half an hour late as it is," I said. Lolly had sat next to her father and Richie, Babsie's son was sitting next to me. Richie looked up from his portable play station (PSP) game.

"Just chillax, Aunty My. Even if we get there late, the important thing is that we all have a good day, yeah?"

My smiled at him. "Out of the mouths of babes," she said.

"You're right you know darling," I said hugging him. "Chillax? What does that mean?"

"You know Aunty Kay... chill and relax."

"Hmm..." I nodded. "Good word."

During the course of the day, I learnt some other new words from Richie and the other young people... almost like a whole new language. Just then Richie's phone rang and this was how the conversation went:

"Yeah... Safe G. What yu on? Me?... Man's jus' on a coach wid di wrinklies bro... Llandudno or somet'ing G... Wales innit? Gonna be at yu gaf later? I'll get onto yu when I get back, yeah... yeah, I'll bell yu... ok later... safe... safe..."

He turned to me and smiled.

"Sorry Aunty Kay. What were you saying now?"

"Er... nothing babes... nothing."

The young generation in England speak their own version of patois and like my Aunt Bliss have the ability to switch between styles automatically from English to traditional patois and their own version of patois. Speech varies I've noticed even between girls and boys and between the north of England and the south. Youth patois incorporates local northern dialect in Manchester and cockney in London. To borrow a familiar phrase from Dr McCoy of Star Trek, "It's patois, Jim, but not as we know it."

Just as slaves developed patois – a fusion of many languages perhaps with a two fold purpose (to communicate among themselves initially and to be able to speak without the slave masters understanding), the black British youth have taken it a step further, developing a new language which their black British parents struggle to understand. Patois has evolved.

"Bungo talk a noh disgrace no more," Mum said. "That's what dem used to call it. These days everybody want to be Jamaican and speak patois even if dem come from Africa. A new fashion; dem change it like dem change clothes."

It was lunchtime when we arrived at our destination in Wales and the weather had become noticeably warmer. The grey sea reflected the colour of the sky but there were some promising blue patches through which the sun peeped, occasionally.

Most people had stripped down to t-shirts. Some braver souls had removed jeans and jogging bottoms and were now in shorts but still clutched umbrellas as they eyed the unpredictable sky suspiciously.

We sat in the large picnic area with purpose built tables and benches near the car park and got out our individual West Indian feasts. The picnic area overlooked the bay and we had a panoramic view of the surrounding landscape. As we ate we batted wasps and other insects away. The joys of picnicking... fishing insects off your fried chicken and out of your ginger beer.

By the time we finished eating, the sky was actually blue with just a few wispy clouds, over rolling green fields of grazing cows, sheep and horses kept in by dry stone walls. The odd farmhouse or country cottage and sleepy villages dotted the landscape looking as if we had stepped back in time, had it not been for the coaches and state-of-the art off road vehicles in the car park. When you live in a large city like Manchester it's easy to forget just how green Britain is and how much open space there actually is.

The mouth-watering aroma of chicken, fish and other spicy traditional food filled the air. Most of the other people using the picnic area discreetly watched us not making any eye contact as they got out their sandwiches and flasks of tea. If we caught them looking, they gave us that nervous instant smile white people have when they are not used to seeing black people so close or in such numbers. You could tell the enlightened ones who had travelled a little. They smiled and struck up conversations with us enquiring where we were from and giving us advice on the places we should visit. Mum shared the contents of her holdall with the family on the table next to her who were happy to abandon their cheese sandwiches and tuck into fried chicken.

Having refuelled in true West Indian style, a few of the younger ones decided to go for a walk up into the hills. Most of us decided to walk down to the beach.

Laughing, we climbed the soft, sliding sand dunes crowned with Mohican tufts of grass like a bad hair day. Silenced, we blinked in wide-eyed wonder at the scene which confronted us beyond the dunes – an unexpected open vastness and blending of watery murky horizon into sullen blue-grey sky. In the distance, white foam broke onto damp brown sugar sand in untidy ragged rolls as the timeless hissing roar of the ocean filled our ears and heads compelling awesome respect.

"Praise the Lord!" Pastor Smilie shouted, as he stood with his family beside him and stared mesmerised, out to sea. I found myself along with others, mouthing the word "Amen," as I reached for Michael's hand.

The kids broke the magical spell. Screaming with buckets and spades in their hands, they ran slipping and sliding down the dunes and unto the damp sand where the tide had gone out about a quarter of a mile. Kicking off sandals and splashing in the cool salt-water pools, they somersaulted, throwing handfuls of sand at each other with shouts of delight. The adults followed with equal glee but at a more sedate pace.

On the dunes behind us, a fickle breeze played, whimsically demolishing and rebuilding.

"Now will you just look at that," Cousin My said in admiration. "Isn't nature wonderful? The breeze is sculpting the sand like coffee icing on a giant cake."

"Praise the Lord!" Pastor Smilie said and we all had to agree.

Those who were brave enough or just foolhardy, paddled in the cold brown sea, shrieking as the waves splashed up their legs. Others like my mother who had come prepared with her wellington boots and cardigan to keep out the chill, stayed a safe distance from the water collecting shells and interesting pebbles. Some spread towels on the dry part of the beech. Then they erected giant multi-coloured umbrellas, protection from sun, breeze or rain, before getting out books and newspapers.

At 4.00pm, having had enough of the cold sea, a few of us decided to start making our way back up the hill to sit in the picnic area. Some of the older kids were kicking a ball about on the compact wet sand. Michael, Ferdie and some of the others decided to walk further up the beach to a little village we had passed earlier.

"Remember you all have to be back at the coach for 5.00pm sharp or wi going without yu!" Cousin My shouted. "We nah leave 'til 5.30pm but if mi tell dem dat dem wi come back at 6.00pm," she whispered.

Of course at 5.00pm, half the people were still missing, including Michael and Ferdie but they all eventually rolled up.

"Weh Richie deh?" Babsie asked.

"Wha' yu mean weh Richie deh? Him noh wid yu?"

"No," Babsie answered. "Mi leave him wid yu."

"Him did a play football pon di beech but mi t'ink seh him come back wid yu!"

"Now look 'ere Ferdie!"

"Ok! So he's not with either of you! I think we've established that," I said. "He knew what time we were leaving."

"Can we give them a few more minutes?" Cousin My asked the coach driver.

The coach driver was looking anxiously at his watch because he wanted to avoid the bank holiday traffic jam on the journey back but he nodded. Cousin Myra did another head count which revealed only Richie and another teenage lad, Jamal, were missing.

"Why dat bwoy caan hear sah?" Babsie said. "I told him not to go off anywhere."

"The last time I saw him was on the beech with Jamal. They were messing about with a rubber dinghy," Lolly said.

Just then a helicopter flew over head, heading out to sea. As we waited, we noticed that people were gathering at the edge of the car park looking down the cliff to the beach and out to sea.

"Looks like something's wrong," the coach driver said. He turned off the engine, got off the coach and walked over to where everyone was standing. A few of us followed him.

"That's the coast guard helicopter and they've just launched the life boat," someone said. "I think someone's in trouble out there."

A man who had been speaking on his mobile phone said,

"Apparently two lads have been washed out to sea in a rubber dinghy."

Babsie started to scream. It was the kind of scream that sounds like an injured animal and sends a shiver down your spine. It brought everybody running off our coach, the other coaches and out of the cars.

"Richie! My baby! Lawd have mercy!" She ran across the road towards the cliff and started to climb over the fence. Ferdie ran after her and grabbed her just in time. It took both him and Uncle Al to hold on to her as she started struggling frantically with them. "Let me go! Let me go! My baby!" she screamed hysterically.

"No Babsie, you don't know if it's him and they might be fine! You can't get to the beech that way, you'll fall over the cliff and get killed!" Ferdie shouted. Absolutely distraught, Babsie wasn't listening and Uncle Al and Ferdie were really struggling to hold on to her. The crowd just looked on in silence. Jamal's grandmother who had ran from the coach was also wailing now.

My mum, who had been trying without success to talk to Babsie, grabbed hold of her and slapped her across her face. The shock stopped Babsie in mid scream and she collapsed into mum's arms sobbing quietly. Mum and Aunty Bliss put their arms around her, and lead her to a nearby bench.

"I've got to go down there and find out what's going on," Ferdie said. Michael was already one step ahead and had already stopped a passing taxi. Babsie got up and started walking quickly towards us.

"No Babsie," Ferdie said. "It's best if you stay here. I'll phone you as soon as I know anything, I promise." Mum and Aunty Bliss took hold of Babsie again as Michael, Ferdie and I jumped into the taxi.

We got to the beech as the life boat was coming in. The large crowd which had gathered, stood watching in complete silence. There was a waiting ambulance with blue light flashing and a couple of police cars. The helicopter was still hovering overhead. Dread shrouded Ferdie's face as we stood and waited with the crowd.

Two coast guards got off the boat followed by two very embarrassed looking teenagers wrapped in blankets. Ferdie let out a sigh of relief and held on to me as his legs almost gave way beneath him. Michael caught hold of his arm as the crowd began to applaud. As Ferdie got his mobile phone out it rang.

"They're all right," he said. "yes… yes. I can see them. They've just got off the boat now… yes walking… they're ok Babs don't cry. Tell Jamal's grandmaddah they're both fine."

Richie and his friend Jamal were taken into the ambulance for a quick check up to make sure they were ok. They then had to give the police a statement but thankfully, what could have been a tragic end to our day trip ended happily, thanks to the Welsh coast guards.

Apparently, Richie and Jamal had found the dinghy on the beech. Obviously, it had been abandoned for a reason but teenage lads' brains don't work that way. When they put it in the water they thought water had just come in over the side not through the hole in the bottom.

They had been happily paddling with their hands and bailing water out until, caught by the current, they had found themselves being washed out to sea. Fortunately, people on the beech had spotted them and alerted the coast guard. Their prompt action no doubt prevented a tragedy.

"Only a bit of water was coming in at first, so we thought we could just paddle back to shore. Then it started rushing into the boat and we started to sink. I knew we were too far out to swim back to the shore besides, the sea was well rough," Richie said.

"It's a good thing the life boat got there in time," Mum said.

"But Aunty Mala, it didn't," Richie answered.

"What do you mean it didn't?" Babsie asked. "So what happened?"

"Well I was just hysterical, yeah, 'cos I was really scared, right," Jamal took up the story. "I thought we was gonna die for sure, man."

"Me too," Richie said. "I was scared too but yu know how we was talkin' 'bout going to church an' dat this morning, yeah, an' I remember dad saying yu don't have to go to church for God to hear you pray, so when I saw how scared Jamal was I just said, 'God please save us'."

Richie stopped and hung his head in embarrassment.

"Well we was still trying to bail out the water, right, then we saw all this greeny-brown stuff in the bottom of the boat," Jamal continued. "Like seaweed or somet'ing, guy, that wasn't there before."

"I think it was sucked up through the hole in the boat," Richie continued. "We started pulling it up to throw it overboard 'cos I thought it was weighing us down. The more I pulled it, it seemed to get stuck in the hole an' then yeah, we realised the water wasn't coming in no more. The seaweed had plugged the hole, yeah."

"Praise the Lord!" Pastor Smilie cried. "The Lord sent His angels to plug the hole."

"Well we just started bailing the water out as fast as we could with our hands and then after a while the life boat came but we would have gone down long before the boat got there if the water hadn't stopped coming in."

"Well, Richie the Lord works in mysterious ways to get our attention," Cousin Myra said.

He certainly does. That experience was a turning point in Richie's life. He started going to church with Cousin Myra and Babsie told me a couple of days ago that he's thinking of getting baptised and he wants to study theology. She said that she and Ferdie have also been going to church more often. Praise the Lord indeed, Pastor Smilie! I'll see you in church next week.

WINTER DRAWS ON

Winter was slow in coming this year. These days the four seasons all seem to meld into one with a common thread of incessant rain. The poor plants are confused. It's November but there are still roses naively clinging to the bushes and the weighty heads of the hydrangea have turned a deep scarlet. Grey squirrels scamper boldly over grass which should have stopped growing, stocking up food for the impending cold spell.

Summer was slow in coming too. In fact, it feels as if we didn't have a summer with all the rain. The old Victorian drains couldn't cope and flooded several properties including mine. It resulted in a neighbourly camaraderie which I hadn't seen for years as, sharing a common enemy, we looked up at the threatening clouds and exchanged tales of ruined goods and advice on damp proofing.

The clocks went back an hour in October and will be put forward again in spring. Day light saving they call it but I'm not sure who's saving the daylight or for what purpose. True the mornings do get lighter for a couple of weeks, but the evenings just suddenly get dark. We wake up in darkness, the days are mostly damp and grey and we come home in darkness. If you catch a glimpse of the sun, you feel as if you've won the lottery and obliged to tell everyone you meet.

The Halloween hordes descended as usual, large and small in scary costumes and painted faces, not minding the rain as they collected a fortune in small change and sweets.

On Bon Fire night, there were fewer fires in gardens this year, making our eyes and noses water in memory of Guy Fawkes and his gunpowder plot. Constantly exploding fireworks frightened the animals and shredded our nerves as they lit up the night sky. Then it was winter, just like that. We knew because on November 6th, the day after Bon Fire night, dawn revealed, as it does every year, an icy cold 'pea super' fog accompanied by a crisp frost. Plastic ice scrapers and cans of de-icer came out of car boots and the backs of cupboards.

We dug out warm clothes, boots, woolly hats, scarves and gloves from bottom drawers and the back of the wardrobes, carefully putting in their place all things summer; sandals, shorts and sleeveless tops. As I shivered wrapped in several layers of clothes, I found it difficult to imagine it ever again being warm enough to wear such things. I made a mental note to get the central heating serviced and the antifreeze in the car checked as I swept up the last of the autumn leaves from the garden. I started stocking up for Christmas from the countless tempting things which had now replaced the Halloween lanterns and costumes.

The phrase 'winter draws on' always comes to mind with a smile at this time of year. I'm not sure who invented it but its 'double entendre' conjures up childhood memories of playground humour. We turned 'draws' to 'drawers' and giggled at the thought of exchanging light summer underwear for large old-fashioned thermal knickers to keep out the chill.

Every year the City Council put on a huge bon fire, fun fair and firework display in various parks across the city, including ours. People come from miles around to see it. My daughters, Laura (Lolly) who is now at Nottingham University and Charlotte (Shari) came over from Nottingham on the train for the day. Shari and her husband Omar live there with their little boy Issy who she brought over to see the family.

Like the changing weather, parenting it seems, has evolved into something completely different to the way it was when I was a child. After enjoying the firework display, we were making our way back to my mother's house nearby when our attention was attracted by the sound of a screaming child. We looked around to see a little girl of about five years old sitting on the ground in the mud. The crowd parted and people walked past warily as the child kicked and shouted abuse at her parents as they tried to reason with her and calm her down. Apparently, she had been refused an expensive glowing toy. As the child continued to scream and began to throw handfuls of mud at her parents, the embarrassed father, himself now covered in mud, apologised to her and running back to the stall, quickly purchased the toy and gave it to her saying,

"We'll have to buy you a new coat now darling. This one's completely ruined."

We all looked at each other in amazement.

"I'm sorry but she wouldn't need a new coat because after I give her a good slap she wouldn't be leaving the house with me again until she's 21," my mother said. I had to agree that here was an occasion when I would make an exception to my no smacking rule.

"A soh di pickney dem stay these days, Missis. Mi t'ink seh a somet'ing ina di food dem a eat," Cousin Myra said. "Even at church yu caan talk to dem an' di parents dem worse. Dem wi cuss yu right there in God's house."

"Hmm..." Aunty Bliss said. "Myra have room fi talk when fi har daughter spoil like rotten pear. Right now a bet she noh know weh Tiana deh." Fortunately, the loud music from the fun fair drowned out most of what Aunty Bliss said.

"Weh yu seh?" Cousin My who was walking on the other side of me asked.

"She said the little girl should hear what har father seh," I cut in quickly, giving Aunty Bliss a hard stare before she could answer.

Cousin My looked puzzled. Lolly started to laugh and I had to step on her foot. Aunty Bliss walked off and started talking to Cousin Babsie. I linked arms with Cousin My.

"Come on," I said. "Let's go to mum's and get warm."

Back at my mother's house, the discussion continued. I found out during the course of the evening that there are as many arguments for as there are against modern parenting.

"Talk about spare the rod and spoil the child," Mum said as she shared out bowls of steaming hot pea soup. "Nowadays, the rod spare 'til it lean up ina corner an' sprout an' turn ina tree."

"But Grandma you must admit that parents were too heavy handed with the belt when you were growing up," Shari said. "They used to beat first and ask questions after."

"Belt!" Mum said. "What belt? Dem would an lick yu wid anyt'ing dem catch… stick…broom… dem would an' all fling stone after yu. If yu noh wan' duck a fi yu business. Yu can stan' up deh mek stone buss yu head."

"But Grandma your generation carried it on," Shari said. "You don't have to beat kids to make them hear you. It's about respect. Mum never beat us and we turned out ok."

My mum looked embarrassed. "Maybe so, Shari, but we weren't as bad as our parents though. That's just the way it was in those days. We thought we were doing it for the best. My mother used to beat the living day lights out of me and it noh kill mi."

"Mum never beat us, Shari," Lolly said, laughing. "She just talked us to death. Daddy would just tell you and stop. Whenever I did anything wrong by the time Mum finished 'giving me a good talking to' as she calls it, I felt so bad I wished she'd just beat me and done."

"Yes, you're right, Lolly. That's what stopped me doing anything wrong; the fear of Mum counselling me and going on and on and on." She put her hand to her mouth and did a mock yawn. Shari and Lolly burst out laughing. It was my turn to be embarrassed.

"I wasn't that bad!" I protested.

"You were!" they both shouted at once.

"Why do you think Lolly is so good at talking herself out of trouble," Shari laughed. "She had to develop a counter strategy, Mum."

"That's not true," I said but everyone was nodding and laughing.

I didn't think it was funny.

"Well yu can't touch even yu own pickney these days or Social Services will come and take them away from you," Mum said. "Dem tek weh Jackie who live across the road little boy last week an' a lie di pickney goh tell pon har a school. Him tell di teacher seh she beat him wid belt because him wouldn't eat him dinner. Jackie say she only slap him because him fling di plate pon di floor. These English pickney dem know dem rights before dem can talk. Dem memorise di phone number for Childline before dem memorise dem own house number. That's why is dem rule di parents dem."

"Noh pickney nah rule mi yu know," Cousin Babsie said. "Mi nah kill dem but as big as they are, mi clap dem backside good and proper when dem need it. Yu let any social worker come say anything to mi. Dem can just tek dem an' noh bring dem back."

"Well mi hear seh di pickney a bawl now an' seh him wan' come home and him all admit seh a lie him tell but dem seh dem have to carry out investigation first," Mum said.

"Is a pity dem noh tek big people," Babsie chuckled. "I was just thinking when my husband get on mi nerves I'd just give him a few licks and send him round to dem office."

"And yu same one gwine run goh back fi him," Mum said, closing the curtains. "Wow, but it really cold out there tonight fi true yu know. A can feel it in mi knee dem. 'Now is the winter of our discontent'. Di man who write dat must have lived in Manchester."

"William Shakespeare in Richard III, Grandma," Lolly said. "I studied it for 'A' level English literature. As far as I know, he's never lived in Manchester."

"Shakespeare? No... it was somebody Beck who wrote that. I read that book," Aunty Bliss said.

"Beckham?" Babsie suggested. "David Beckham wrote that I think. When he realised England wasn't going to win the World Cup."

"No not the football player, Babsie" Aunty Bliss said impatiently.

"John Steinbeck, Aunty Bliss," Shari said, looking at Babsie. "He borrowed the title from Shakespeare."

"Yes, that's the one about a man in America who put money before everything. Somebody give mi last Christmas."

"Whoever write it, it still cold outside," Mum said.

"Yes it look like it's going to be a bad winter this year. Even the Bible warn us about winter you know in Matthew 24," Cousin My said. "It says we should pray that our flight isn't in the winter."

A look of pure mischief came onto Babsie's face as she winked at me. I had suspected that she had thrown in the David Beckham red herring on purpose.

"So what yu saying Cousin My, Jesus warned us about going on a flight from Manchester Airport in winter?" she asked. Shari nearly choked on a mouthful of soup as she tried not to laugh. Everyone turned and looked at Babsie.

"What?" she asked innocently. "Well He could walk on water and He knew what was going to happen in the future. Maybe He teleported himself into the future, like in those science fiction films and saw the planes all backing up at the airport because of the fog."

Cousin Myra gave Babsie a long serious look. The rest of us were really struggling to keep a straight face now.

Cousin My cleared her throat. "Babsie, sometimes I really worry 'bout you. If yu noh know what yu saying, just shut yu mout' before yu blaspheme. A going to ask Pastor Smilie to pray fi yu, yu hear."

"Only joking Cousin My, sorry," Babsie said, giving her a hug.

"There are some things yu don' joke 'bout Barbara," Cousin My said, pushing her away.

"Sorry," Babsie said again. "In my opinion the problem with the kids really started with banning Christian prayers in school. Yes, that was definitely when everything started going downhill," she added trying to redeem herself.

"No," Mum said. "A when di government stop people from beat di pickney dem and ban di cane and di strap in school. That's when dem start pulling knife an' gun pon teacher."

"No, no, it was when they started turning all those beautiful churches into restaurants and night clubs," Cousin My said. "Sacrilege!"

"Well Aunty most of those churches were empty every Sunday anyway," Lolly said. "At least now the buildings have been preserved and are being put to good use instead of being left derelict."

"No, it's poor parenting and all these do-gooders making excuses for out of control youths who have everything given to them on a plate in this country and just waste it," Shari said. "I see them every day in court."

"They should bring back National Service an' send dem all to Pakistan to fight," Mum said. We all looked at her puzzled until the penny dropped.

"Do you mean Afghanistan, Grandma?" Shari asked.

"Yes... same 'ting. Send dem goh fight mek dem stop beat up old people fi dem few likkle penny."

"The answer is not that simple, Mum," I said. "Times have changed and people have changed."

"Times have changed, Kelly," Cousin My said, "but people did bad from morning."

"Yu right My," Aunty Bliss said. "Even di people dem in di Bible did bad like hell an' God have to rough dem up fi get dem fi do wha' Him want. With newspapers, television and internet, we just hear 'bout dem badness more now."

The discussion went on 'til late. We wrapped the sleeping Issy in a blanket before strapping him into his car seat. Then we all wrapped up against the frost that was settling on the ground and the fog that had started to descend and went to our respective homes.

The next day Lolly got a taxi to catch the first train back to Nottingham she had an early lecture. As I was scraping ice off the windscreen of the car to give Shari a lift to the train station, Issy came out of the house and ran excitedly towards a patch of ice.

"No Issy, stop!" I shouted but ignoring me, he continued.

Unfortunately, the patch of ice, as I suspected, was a puddle with just a thin frozen layer on top and it gave way leaving him standing ankle deep in muddy water. At that moment his mother came out of the house. Now when I was three years old, if I had done that my mother would have given me what she calls 'a slap ina mi headside' and ask me why I was 'soh fool fool'.

Following on from the discussion the night before about parenting, I said nothing and watched to see what Shari would do. Issy and his mother looked at each other.

"Oh dear," Shari said calmly. "Now that was a bit silly. I heard Nanny tell you to stop. Why did you disobey Nanny? Now you'll have to go back inside and change." Issy walked out of the puddle with his head down.

"Am I a Silly Billy Mummy?"

"Yes," Shari replied. "Look at you."

"Oh dear," Issy repeated, "Sorry Mummy."

"And what do you need to say to Nanny?" Shari asked with raised eyebrows. Issy walked over to me with an embarrassed smile and hugged my legs.

"Sorry for disbaying you Nanny."

There's a lot to be said for modern parenting. There might be hope for the future after all.

The traffic was unusually heavy as people who would normally leave their cars at home took them out for their first winter airing. Fumes bellowed from exhausts and blended with the fog. The gritters had not been caught off guard this year. The trucks had been out overnight spraying the roads with salt and sand to melt the ice.

Feeling as if I was taking my life in my hands, I put the heater on full, wiped the condensation from the windscreen and edged cautiously into the bumper-to-bumper car wars of tooting horns and flashing lights. I was forced to slam on my brakes as a car suddenly appeared from nowhere and cut into the space the driver on the main road had kindly made for me. My first instinct was to give the driver a two-finger gesture, especially as he was driving my dream car, the BMW X6. Just in time, I remembered my grandson in the back who was watching me keenly and making vroom vroom noises.

"Is he a naughty man, Nanny?" he asked.

"Yes dear," I answered.

"Does he need five minutes on the naughty step?"

"I think he does," I smiled.

"A good slap ina him head side more like," Shari mumbled reaching for a tissue. She had been putting on her lipstick and the jolt had made her smear it right across her cheek.

"Pardon Mummy?" Issy asked.

"Nothing, Baby. He's a very naughty man."

I had to laugh remembering the conversation the night before. Shari is a lawyer and I suddenly had a vision of her in court saying:

"Your Honour, I recommend that the defendant is not given a two month custodial sentence. Just give him a lick ina him head side." The prisons would definitely be less crowded I mused as I pulled out into the traffic and silently asked God to stretch out his calming hand and pour oil on the turbulent waters of the day ahead.

I had settled into the crawling traffic on Princess Parkway when a cyclist, on a racing bike with pencil thin wheels, whizzed past me with inches to spare. He cut across the car in front forcing the driver to brake.

"Bloody hell!" I shouted before I could stop myself. "What an idiot!"

"Mum!" Shari said, looking over her shoulder.

"Oops!" I said looking at the grandson through the rear view mirror and hoping he hadn't heard me; no such luck.

"Where's the idiot, Nanny?" he asked looking out of the window.

"Er... it' just another naughty man, Issy; he's gone now."

"Where's he gone? Bloody hell!" said the little voice in the back. Shari buried her face in her hands. "Mum…" she groaned.

"Sorry."

The cyclist was quickly disappearing in the fog. His skin-tight lycra shorts and t-shirt were totally unsuitable for the weather but at least he wore a fluorescent vest over his backpack as he continued to weaved dangerously between the cars. So intent was he to show off his physique or his riding skills, that he appeared blissfully unaware of the clenched fists and other hand gestures he was getting from motorists who were braking and swerving in an effort not to kill him. He turned his head and gave a finger gesture when one motorist, who not having an impressionable three year old in the back of the car, wound down his window and shouted with a few choice expletives what an idiot he was. The cyclist's craggy weather beaten face didn't go with the body and he really looked old enough to have known better.

"Those shorts must be squeezing his brain as well as his bits," I said crossly.

"Squeezing his bits?" asked the little parrot in the back seat.

Shari started to laugh. "Do you know Mum, you're getting more like Grandma every day."

"I don't know what you mean," I said smiling.

"You just need to be a bit more careful what you say in front of Little Big Ears there," she whispered. "I've only just got him to substitute 'Oh dear' for 'Jesus Christ' which he heard his dad say recently."

I looked at Issy again in the rear view mirror who was looking at us with large innocent eyes, taking every single word out of our mouths.

"I've got a swear box now for Omar. Every time he swears, he has to put a pound in it. October was not a good month for him. I've got enough now for a new pair of shoes," Shari chuckled.

"I think you'd better get a swear box for Issy as well," I said. "You'll soon have enough for a handbag too."

On the way back from the train station, I drove past Alexandra Park, infamous for its muggings and gang related crimes. The fog had lifted considerably and the park was suddenly transformed into a surreally alien landscape as the sun broke through the clouds, illuminating the mist and silhouetting the trees. The stark branches and few leaves which still hung on defiantly, were turned to burnished gold. The frost on the grass was like a hazy carpet of grey over which the mist writhed sullenly as it began to lift.

The ducks, looking depressed, huddled together in the only corner of the pond that wasn't frozen. They watched the early morning joggers of every shape and size, huffing and puffing along the path, with dispassionate eyes. The joggers and dog walkers throwing sticks, like the cars, emitted condensation from their mouths and noses like an old steam locomotive.

The fog had completely lifted by the time I reached home but the sky had clouded over and I was thinking that it was feeling cold enough for snow, when the first white flakes began to fall. Shivering, with my only thought being to make myself a hot cup of tea to warm my frozen fingers, I opened the front door. There was loud music coming from upstairs. The sound stopped me in my tracks with a puzzled frown because I was certain I hadn't left the radio on. The only other people living in the house were my daughter Lolly who had already phoned to tell me she'd made it in time for her lecture in Nottingham. Michael, my partner, was even further away – two hundred miles away in fact, working just outside London.

"Hello!" I shouted, hesitantly, but there was no answer.

I climbed the stairs apprehensively. As I reached the landing, I saw that the bathroom door was wide open and the radio was on the stool with the extension lead coming from my bedroom.

"What the…"

The shower curtains were drawn and I could hear the sound of water. Someone was having a shower!

"Er…hello!" I called again but with the noise of the radio and water from the shower, whoever it was couldn't hear me. The thought did cross my mind just to run out of the house but I tip toed into my bedroom and got the window pole. The loose floorboard on the landing which I've asked Michael several times to fix, squeaked and made me jump. Cold sweat prickling my armpits. I pulled myself together and heart beating, adrenalin pumping, I continued my tip toed creep towards the bathroom.

As I reached the open door, the water stopped abruptly and the shower curtain was thrown back. I don't know which one of us screamed the loudest – me or my cousin Babsie. The look on Babsie's face was a picture and I'm sure it reflected mine as she stood open mouthed in the shower, dripping wet in all her glory. On her head was a pair of Lolly's knickers instead of a shower cap. She recovered before I did.

"Lawd have mercy, Kelly! Wha wrong wid yu man! Yu nearly give mi heart attack! A wha yu did a goh do wid dat?" She indicated the pole in my hand.

I was speechless as with no inhibitions, she climbed out of the shower, took the window pole out of my hand, leaned it up in a corner and still stark naked marched into my bedroom. I finally found my voice.

"Babsie! How on earth did you get in? And what are you doing in my shower?"

"How yu mean how mi get in? Yu fool fool. Through the door of course!" I think she realised that my puzzled expression meant I required a more thorough explanation and added.

"Look how many years yu keep the spare key in the same place in the garden. Weh di towel dem deh? Yu wan' mi fi freeze to death?"

I made a mental note to find a new hiding place for the spare key. Michael had been telling me to for some time.

"Why have you got Lolly's knickers on your head?" I asked before I remember Babsie's son Richie's revelation at her 50th birthday party that she wore her knickers on her head in the shower.

"Well it clean!" she said defensively. "Mi forget mi shower cap and fi yu drawers dem too big."

I was about to say something cutting regarding the reference to the size of my bottom but I thought I'd let that one pass for the moment.

"Why are you in my house having a shower?" I asked again.

"Di central heating break down last night an' wi noh have noh hot water. A long time mi a tell Ferdie fi get one a dem service 'ting deh wid di Gas Board weh yu an' Michael have but him noh listen. Now yu see wha'ppen?" Babsie kissed her teeth.

"'Bout him a goh come wid mi fi share shower. Mi just tell him fi goh a Aunty Mala an' gwaan a work."

"So what about the kids?"

"Dem stay wid Cousin Myra last night. She ina dat big house she an' Tiana one since George run way left har."

Babsie started to chuckle. "Mi an' Ferdie squing up all night under di quilt and share one hot water bottle we find ina di attic. Bwoy is di best night mi hav fi a long time... hee hee hee! Mi noh get a wink a sleep."

"You could have told me you were coming," I said.

"Kelly," Babsie said patiently. "Mi noh know wha' wi a goh do wid you yu know. Mi left message on yu house phone and two on yu mobile. Wha' yu have mobile phone fah if yu keep it in di bottom of yu handbag? Goh mek mi a cup a tea noh? Mi noh eat nut'n from morning."

When I came back with the tea, my cousin was dressed, having helped herself to my anti-perspirant, moisturising cream and perfume.

"Mi seh, Kelly, di temperature drop soh sudden, it tek everybody by surprise. Mi lef some clothes outside pon di line last night. When mi get up this morning, dem stiff like board – frozen solid. Mi have fi bring dem inside fi thaw dem out. Mind you it soh cold in di house dem probably still frozen. Ferdie trousers dem stan' up like him ina dem."

Later when I related the story to Michael, expecting sympathy, he just laughed.

"You should have known straight away that it was one of your crazy family," he said. "Why would a burglar be having a shower in a house he's trying to rob? And what have I told you about that window pole? One a these days somebody going to lick yu in yu head wid it. Kelly if you think somebody in the house, just run man and call the police. Yu 'tink yu a superwoman?"

The next day as I snuggled into the armchair in front of the glowing imitation coal fire and looked out onto my garden covered in two inches of fluffy white snow, I had one of my nostalgic moments. I remembered sitting like that as a little girl in the late sixties in front of a roaring coal fire with smoke going up the chimney; fascinated by the very latest invention, colour television. The bubble burst, however, as I remembered my job next morning was to clean out the ashes from the fire grate. Then I had to go into the utility room, and fill the battered soot covered bucket with coal from the cupboard and make the fire, ready for lighting again in the evening.

We lived in a block of flats and the cupboard was filled from a chute outside on the communal landing. The coal men, covered in soot themselves, drove a huge truck, stacked with sacks of coal. They would climb noisily up the stairs in hobnail boots, carrying the sacks on their backs and empty them even more noisily down the chute. I shuddered at the memory and thanked the Lord for modern inventions. It was in those days that we really saw fog, almost every day for the entire winter months and the buildings were black with soot from the coal fires. Life seemed simpler and safer then though.

Nowadays, the buildings have been washed clean and fog is rare. Real coal fires are becoming fashionable again but only with those who didn't experience them first time around in a damp and draughty house. They are welcome to them. I just click my fire on… hey presto… instant burning coals and no mess. The only drawback is when the gas bill arrives.

To me, these days the phrase 'winter draws on' no longer just has the obvious slightly 'risqué' double meaning it had in the days of my youth. As I get older I become more and more grateful for my family, my relatives, for the warmth we share, the good old fashioned West Indian traditions we respect and value. Sometimes I am disheartened by so-called modern-day advancement. For years I have observed winter creeping into many aspects of society; a coldness seems to have arrived where simple love for your fellow man is concerned and frozen out basic standards of courtesy.

HAPPY HOLIDAYS

Jingle bells…jingle bells… jingle all the way. On the first day of Christmas my true love sent to me… Ho! Ho! Ho!... A partridge in a pear tree! Yes, it's that time of year again and my head is buzzing. I'm suffering from sensory over load. I went shopping in the local supermarket today…We three kings of Orient are… bearing gifts… Aaahhhhh! I now need to go and take a couple of aspirins and have a lie down.

I remember one year my daughter Lolly coming to me in all innocence when she was about six years old and asking,

"Mum, where is Oriantar?" I looked at her puzzled.

"What do you mean, love?"

"You know… Oriantar where the three kings came from. Which country is that?" The innocence of children.

The weather has changed again from frosty to mild and wet. Did I say wet? There has been extensive flooding in several areas of the country and I don't mean the kind of flooding we had at the beginning of the year when our basements were flooded by the old Victorian drains. I mean floods of near Biblical proportions with huge bridges that have stood for decades washed away and people killed. I find it difficult to believe that this is England as I watch terrified people on the news being rescued by rubber dinghies going down the streets. Others were air lifted by helicopter from the roofs of their flooded homes while murky water swirled below them.

It seems that moisture which should at this time of year be falling as snow or be somewhere else all together, is falling on Britain as rain possibly due to the global warming the scientists keep warning us about. Why am I complaining? It's 9 degrees Centigrade in Manchester today; it's minus 7 in Scotland. What's to complain about? Even though scientists have been warning us about the rapidly depleting ozone layer since I was a girl, the catastrophe now seems to be upon us but no-one heeded the warnings.

"There's nothing new there in human history, Kelly," my cousin Myra said." I just wonder sometimes if this is all part of God's plan and if everything is just simply unfolding as it should." We were sitting in the dining room which looked out onto the garden at my mother's house.

Mum looked out despondently onto her garden. She is a keen gardener and grows her own vegetables with which she keeps us all supplied. Michael says it keeps her out of mischief. "Di poor plant dem really turn fool fi true," she said.

The spring bulbs were already pushing their way out of soil which should have been frozen.

"At this rate we're going to have crocuses and daffodils for Christmas instead of spring," Mum said.

"Hmm... yu pumpkin dem noh nice this year at all, Ma," Cousin My said.

"Yes, mi know. Mi have fi plant dem late soh dem noh have time fi full. Mi hardly get anyt'ing out a mi garden dis year. Either dem rotten wid di rain or slug eat dem."

"Never mind Mum, the beans and spring onions were nice," I said trying to cheer her up.

"Hmm... a suppose soh," Mum said.

"Mala a soh di decorations ina di new people dem house nice," Cousin My said.

"A stupid dem stupid," Mum said. "Dem put up di Christmas tree from dem move ina di house in October. Dem have one little yoot deh, him noh look like him goh a school at all. A him mi si put dem up. Mi see him ina di corner shop yesterday. Him come ask me if mi can buy a pack of cigarette and two can a lager fi him."

"Den yu buy it, Ma?" My asked.

"Mi! Missis yu t'ink mi mad? Him seh a fi him faadah but mi still nah buy it. Him come ina di shop a argue wid di man because dem tell him seh him too young fi buy beer and cigarette," Mum said.

I looked out at the house which was covered in multi coloured lights with an inflatable Santa Claus sitting on the roof. Each year the Christmas decorations go up earlier and are more elaborate with people competing with each other to decorate the outsides of their houses. I wonder if some people even bother to take them down from one year to the next. The young man, who I assumed mum was talking about appeared at the window, making another addition to his decorations. I was very tempted to go and knock on the door of the house and ask,

"What does Christmas mean to you? What is the significance?" I imagined the possible ensuing scenario: the teenager would tell me that it's about who can buy the most expensive electronic gadgets for their children or who can eat the most or get the most drunk. I would make an attempt at light-hearted conversation, dropping the names of Jesus and God in subtly. The youth would then call back over his shoulder,

"Dad, it's those Christian nut cases again! What? No not the Jehovah's Witnesses! This ones alone and not as well dressed! Shall we call the police and have her arrested for using offensive language in front of a minor or should we just beat her up ourselves?"

The father would answer from his permanent place on the sofa in front of the TV, with cigarette hanging from his mouth and surrounded by several empty cans of lager.

"Er.. what? Miner? Where's the miner, son?"

"No not miner, Dad, minor... me... you know, under age kid like me."

"Oh... right you are, son."

"Clear off, lady, before I get my social worker onto you. I know my rights you know. My social worker's told me that no-one can make me do anything. That's why I don't go to school anymore."

The father would now appear at the door.

"What did the foul mouth Christian say to you, son? She didn't use that word 'Jesus' or 'God' in front of you did she?" He would spit as if to cleanse the taste of the words from his mouth. "Lady you should be ashamed of yourself. Now clear off before we call his social worker and have you investigated."

It is at this point that I would notice the skull and National Front swastika next to the 'peace on earth and goodwill to all men' plaque. The idiot left brain side of me that had made me knock the door in the first place, would now be over-ridden by the sensible, self-preserving right brain side which would now be screaming, "Get the hell out of here! Run and don't lead them back to your mother's house!"

The youth and his father would invite all their friends and neighbours to join in while they chase me down the street with meat cleavers and baseball bats. The community police officers would lean nonchalantly on their bicycles and look the other way as I run past followed by the mob. If they are in a good mood, they may ask me as I run past screaming, if I'm gay, a minor or if either of my parents occupy an influential position in government, to which I would answer "No". They would then shout that they can't help me as it's not in their remit this year and ride off in the opposite direction. If I'm really lucky and it's been a quiet day, they may arrest me for breaching the peace, thus saving my life. Over-active imagination you say? Maybe, but not too far from the truth. Just watch this space.

Michael was home this weekend after working all week in Nottingham with his brothers. I'm glad he took that job in Nottingham. It meant he could stay with our daughter Shari and husband Omar plus spend some time with our little grandson, Issy. Michael tells me Shari has, with some difficulty, managed to get Issy to substitute "Wow!" for "Bloody Hell!" which he picked up from me, completely by accident I might add, the last time they were in Manchester.

I didn't feel like cooking on Sunday and neither did Michael so as it was just the two of us, we decided to go down to the Trafford Centre for dinner. Now for anyone who's never heard of the Trafford Centre, it is described as a large indoor shopping centre located in the metropolitan Borough of Trafford, part of Greater Manchester. I think that is quite an understatement. I believe it is actually one of the largest shopping centres in Europe and one of the biggest temples of worship to capitalism that I have ever seen. It actually looks like a cross between an awesome giant temple and showy elaborate palace with its multi coloured domes and towers lighting up the night sky and visible for miles around. I would imagine so spectacular is its lighting that it may even be visible from outer space.

As we approached the Trafford Centre, Christmas trees surrounded by prancing reindeers twinkled with electric blue stars on the roundabout which fed traffic into the Centre. The reindeers changed colour from red, to green to blue as we watched. The startling blue was repeated in the mock icicles clinging to the tower and the walls of the building opposite the roundabout. The vehicles slowed to a crawl but for once no-one minded as it gave us a chance to take in the amazing decorations.

Even though the Orient Car Park said full, Michael, ever the optimist, decided to take his chances. The Centre is divided into four different sections and the Orient is where all the restaurants and the cinema are. We passed the coach park which was filled with what must have been near to two hundred coaches which had carried shoppers from other cities and from the Continent.

We struggled for over half an hour, using guile and subterfuge to outwit other motorists trying to get a parking space which was like gold. When that didn't work because other motorists were wilier than we were, we decided to copy some others and stalk shoppers coming out of the Centre as they made their way back to their cars. We cackled and gloated in triumph like Ebenezer Scrooge at the look of elation followed by devastation on the face of a driver who was stalking our victim too, only to realise at the last minute that we had spotted them first and had already positioned ourselves to claim the prize of the golden parking bay.

I thought there might have been a heated exchange of words and rude gestures as we had already seen several times between other motorists but like a true sportsman, the driver of the other car conceded defeat with a smile and a cheery wave. Safe in the knowledge that the bay was ours, after experiencing that same disappointment, we could afford to smile back now sympathetically while we tried not to look too smug. As we got out of our car, someone unexpectedly pulled out and drove away and our fellow competitor gave us the thumbs up sign as he quickly claimed his space.

Giggling like children Michael and I walked into the building past the rippling water of the fountain, under the blank eyes of the marble unicorns, other mythical creatures and Roman figures, blowing golden trumpets. Stone lions, with equally lifeless eyes, graced the outer courtyards at measured intervals between the giant pillars. We climbed the terracotta and cream steps of The Great Hall, made from finest marble in China, to the dozens of bars, cafes and restaurants offering every kind of food imaginable. The hall boasts the largest and most spectacular chandelier in the world also made in China. The restaurant area looked out over the food hall on the ground floor, modelled down to the life buoys and lifeboats on that ill-fated ship, The Titanic. The food hall houses all the fast food outlets such as McDonald and KFC under a ceiling modelled on the night sky complete with twinkling stars which faded in an out at intervals.

We avoided the lines of statues of sphinxes and pharaohs lining the walls and cleverly leading you to the miles of inviting shops touting jewellery and brand names to suit every size and taste. These shops, all use the latest brain washing retail techniques to catch your interest and pull you in, while all the time the incessant merry music...jingle bells... jingle bells...Ho! Ho! Ho! Ho! The jokes on you while we mesmerise you with sublime lighting and sale signs, we fleece you of every penny in your purse or wallet or take you beyond the limit of your credit card. We wish you a merry Christmas... Ho! Ho! Ho! Ho! ... and a suicidal New Year when your bank statement arrives in January.

We had a lovely meal and I resisted the temptation of the shopping mall. When we got home, I decided to lie down for a while and fell asleep. I had the most horrendous nightmare about cartoon Santas laughing maniacally while I was being chased by ferocious unicorns which were swept away in a swollen river of twenty pound notes. Michael said it was the cheese balls I had for starters with my meal.

It's a family tradition in our house for us to go downstairs Christmas morning in our nightclothes. I make hot chocolate and toast, we put the fire on in the living room and the Christmas tree lights and open our presents.

Throughout the Christmas holiday, my extended family usually get together at a different relative's house for dinner each day. Generally, this is fine but it can get slightly out of hand and end in people falling out.

This year it was unanimously decided that each family would spend Christmas day in their own house due to the events last year. Last year Christmas dinner was at our house. All went well until we broke out the chocolate liqueurs after the Queen's speech. Alcohol is a wonderful lubricant. At the same time it loosens the tongue it seems to loosen the screws of the brain and people begin to feel this is a good time to speak their mind. For once, it wasn't my mother. My aunt Beverley, she who is also known as Bliss, although sometimes I seriously wonder why, took it upon herself to tell my cousin Myra a few home truths about her parenting skills or lack of it. Now, I know most of what Aunty Bliss said was true. We have all thought it over the years but everyone agreed that this was not a good time to criticise Cousin My as her husband George walked out on her just before Christmas.

Yes Aunty Bliss, I know you felt obliged to tell My, "for her own good" and she "needed to be told", but I really think you could have phrased it a little more delicately.

"Yu pickney spoil like rotten pear an' yu husband right fi run weh lef yu", were not the best choice of words on this occasion. Cousin My was looking for sympathy when she started crying into her fifth glass of sherry. Mum is right, if you had given My that sympathy then she might not have thrown the rest of her sherry in your face and come on, she had drank nearly all of it. There couldn't have been more that a couple of spoonfuls in that glass.

Yes, I know you didn't know My's daughter, Tiana, had walked into the room, and no, calling you a "stupid old cow" was not very nice but that's Tiana. She doesn't think she's rude and she loves her mother.

When you stormed out, you knew full well there were no taxis running and that Uncle Al had finished the half bottle of brandy so he was in no fit state to drive. So, if you had to walk five miles home in your high heels, you have no-one to blame but yourself. Please tell me, how did you expect poor Uncle Al, drunk as he was and unable to walk a straight line, to carry you on his back the last three miles without falling over? It wasn't his fault you "mash up" your knee, as you put it.

I don't think the police had any choice but to arrest you both when they saw you rolling about on the ground after Uncle Al fell over with you for the second time. It could have had something to do with all the shouting you were doing and Uncle Al being completely incoherent - nothing at all to do with racism. Anyway, you managed to convince them, eventually... at the station, that you really weren't fighting. So that turned out all right. Although the officer was adamant that he saw you punch Uncle Al. Uncle Al was just angry when he told them he wanted to press charges and that they should lock you up for the night. They saw the funny side of it... eventually.

At least you got a lift home, never mind what the neighbours thought. The police officer did explain to you that the riot van was all they had available and that he really did press the button for the flashing lights and siren by accident outside your house.

By the way, Aunty Bliss, the police do not have Uncle Al listed in their files as a victim of domestic violence. Stop worrying; they're not watching you – they've got better things to do.

On a personal note, I did tell Michael that under no circumstances was he getting into that car to come after you. He had helped Uncle Al to finish the brandy and he needs his driving licence. No, he wasn't lying when he told you that I hid the car key down my bra. Yes, Michael does wear the trousers in our house and if I hear you've been calling him a wimp again you and I might have to fall out.

Mum, I'm very sorry if we got a bit carried away when Michael was trying to get the car key out of my bra. We were in our bedroom with the door closed at the time if you remember. We didn't know you were "asleep" in Lolly's bedroom. Maybe you wouldn't have heard so much if you hadn't had your wine glass pressed against the wall. The story that you thought it was Lolly and her boyfriend Steven messing about and that you were just trying to stop her from getting herself into trouble and ruining her life like I did just won't wash. Please understand, once and for all that getting pregnant with Shari did not ruin my life.

Now, come on Uncle Al, Pastor Franklin did explain that when Michael said that none of you should put your foot in his rahtid house again, it was just a figure of speech. So that's all right, isn't it? I gave Michael a good talking to when he sobered up and he assures me that he really didn't mean it and he doesn't even remember saying that. If any of you want to stay overnight when you visit us, you can now because Michael isn't sleeping in the spare room anymore.

Now I've got all that off my chest, I'm so glad we're all friends again. We had some very good family get-togethers this year. I really missed seeing you guys for the whole of January and February. I've already thanked Pastor Franklin and Pastor Smilie for being such good mediators. They could teach Kofi Annan a thing or two. Cousin Myra has taken Pastor Smilie's advice and has put less rum in the Christmas cake this year and she will be drinking non-alcoholic wine. She's also started her counselling sessions to help her come to terms with her husband leaving.

So family, I'll see you all this year, after, the Queens speech for sherry and mince pies at our house. I've bought a different brand of liqueurs, not as strong, this year. There will be the usual games of monopoly and scrabble.

Oh by the way Cousin Babsie, 'phoning a friend' is not allowed in scrabble; that's cheating. While I'm at it, you should know by now that 'qqxxzptt' is not a word in the English dictionary, so please don't box the scrabble board across the room and walk out again this year. I do not consider you, my brother John Joseph and Shari (two graduates) against me and Issy to be fairly matched teams, no matter how much Issy's speech has come on since he had his third birthday.

I'm dreaming of a table groaning under it's weight of turkey and assorted meats. The best china and glassware and Bing Crosby "I'm Dreaming of a White Christmas" serenading us in the background. Dream on Bing. The white Christmas isn't happening this year, mate... wet but not white. We're still going to have a great time though.

As I sit here watching the roses nodding in the breeze, the rain has stopped for the moment. The grey squirrels look as if they're not bothering to hibernate this winter. They're doing summersaults on the grass as they eat the breadcrumbs put out for the birds. An outraged robin watches them from the fence, fluffing up it's feathers in annoyance but the cat from next door soon sees them off. At the sight of the cat, Michael is immediately alert. His eyes narrow and he looks up at his home-made catapult hanging behind the back door. He has still not forgiven the cat since it knocked over the bowl of chicken and ran off with some of it when the men had their barbecue.

"Not today, Michael," I said as he made to get up. "Leave the cat alone, it's nearly Christmas. Surely you can extend peace on earth and good will to all men to the poor cat." Michael thought about it for a while.

"Okay, Babes. Just for you. We'll call a temporary truce until after Christmas, then watch out puss. It will be open season on your backside."

VALENTINE

Like Christmas and Easter, Valentine's Day seems to have been hijacked in recent years by commercialism. Hotels offer romantic breaks, restaurants offer dinner packages, while stores great and small tout cards, flowers and chocolates to enable people to express love and admiration in the name of St Valentine. In some cases it is to assuage guilty feelings for love that should have been expressed throughout the year in those little caring words and actions.

Whenever my family get together, it always results in an interesting debate about some current topic or other. The topic on this occasion last year was Valentine's Day which was looming. Some of the men were anxious all the women were hopeful and had been dropping hints for some time that a new iron or vacuum cleaner was not considered to be a romantic Valentine's present. They might just get away with a new mobile phone or ipod... especially if it came with flowers or low calorie chocolates.

The shops were full of red and pink hearts, ribbon festooned cards and boxes of chocolates, not to mention flowers, the prices of which had rocketed in a few days. If you weren't in love then it was a pretty depressing time. If you thought you were loved or there was the tiniest chance you might have a secret admirer, and you woke up on Valentine's Day to find the post man had only delivered the gas bill then it could be difficult to get through the day without biting some one's head off as you plotted revenge on the offender.

Of course my family as usual had their own unique take on Valentine's Day.

"A wonder a who start all this foolishness anyway?" my mother asked. "Dem have a lot to answer for." I wondered why she seemed so cross until I remembered that when my father was alive, he always brought home a large bunch of flowers for her on Valentine's Day. Even though my father had died a long time ago, the day still brought back sad memories for her.

My youngest daughter Laura, Lolly to us, felt the need to give us a history lesson... a very interesting one though I might add which I thought was worth sharing.

"There are lots of different versions of how Valentine's day started Grandma," Lolly said. "One story is that the Roman Emperor Claudius II, decided that single men made better soldiers than those with wives and families so he outlawed marriage for young men."

"Bwoy dem Romans deh noh did easy yu know," my cousin Myra said. "I can't see how that would help anything. That could only lead to fornication and a lot of illegitimate children."

"Well I don't know about that you know Aunty My," Lolly said, "but Valentine who was a priest, thought it wasn't fair so he defied Claudius' decree and continued to marry lovers in secret. He was put to death when Claudius found out."

"Well St Valentine have the last laugh," Mum said, "because who has ever heard of Claudius Day?"

"Another version of the story, Grandma," Lolly continued, "is that St Valentine was killed for trying to help early Christians to escape from prison in Roman times."

"Oh that might explain why they made him a saint," Cousin My said.

"Maybe Aunty My but they say he was sent to prison himself and sent the first Valentine's card or note while he was in prison to the jailer's daughter who he fell in love with. He signed it "From your Valentine" and that's why we put that on our Valentines cards today."

"So why the 14th of February, Lolly?" Mum asked.

"I think it was either the day St Valentine died or the day he was buried, Grandma, but some say it was actually the date of Lupercalia."

"Lupa what?" Mum asked. "It sounds like a disease."

"Lupercalia, it's a pagan fertility festival in honour of spring. Christians just tried to Christianise it by making it Valentine's day."

"Hmm... Mi know seh fertility have to come into it somewhere. Why these people caan behave good?" Mum said.

"A soh everything mix up these days, Ma. We have to be careful we don't get caught up in all sorts of things we don't understand. Pastor Smiley was telling us that even some of the things we do at Christmas and Easter have links with paganism. That's a nice story anyway Lolly," Cousin My said. "That just goes to show that some men can be faithful til death. Dem noh all run weh leave you at the first sign of trouble." Mum cleared her throat and quickly changed the subject before Cousin My could continue.

Cousin Myra's husband, George, left her just before Christmas, three years ago. Myra didn't take it well and it has been the topic of many conversations in our family which usually end with Myra in tears.

Last Christmas it caused a great falling out resulting in the family needing the mediation services of Pastor Franklin from the Seventh Day Adventist church and Pastor Smiley from the Church of God of Prophecy. Following Pastor Smiley's suggestion of counselling, My had also taken up yoga and now has a new outlook on life. Her new found zeal for life could also have something to do with Tomek, her new 'gentleman' as she calls him. It seems love is in the air.

Tomek is a Polish limousine driver who we met when one of my other cousins, Babsie decided to celebrate her 50th birthday in style last year. While driving us to the party at the West Indian Centre, the limo had become stuck on the corner of Westwood Street, resulting in a traffic jam, a crowd of onlookers and our pictures on the front page of the local newspaper. Babsie looked like a film star in her floor length ball gown and tiara. My mother had felt obliged to assist the two community police officers, Phil and Darren, as they tried to re-direct the traffic so the stuck limo could be manoeuvred back onto the main road. The picture of mum arm in arm with Phil and Darren looked as if she was being arrested when they were really trying to get her out of the middle of the road so she wouldn't be killed.

They say every picture tells a story, but don't believe it. Every picture only tells half a story and even that half isn't always what it seems when a journalist who wants to sell papers is behind the pen.

Anyway, back to Tomek. He had dropped such heavy hints about not knowing anyone in Manchester and that he was finishing his shift after dropping us off and going home alone, that Babsie had felt obliged to invite him to her birthday party. The only problem was that at first it seemed Tomek had taken a shine to me although I didn't realise. I didn't even get the clue when at the party my partner Michael who was master of ceremony, had come off the stage and had pointedly hauled Tomek away and introduced him to Cousin Myra. I just thought Tomek was being really friendly when he put his arm around my shoulder as he showed me the pictures of his farm in Poland. To everyone's surprise, given Myra's declared hatred for all men, they had got on really well resulting in Myra inviting Tomek to church. She had been giving him bible studies since and helping him with his English. The only problem was that Tomek was now speaking English with a strong Jamaican accent.

Having finished her story about St Valentine, Lolly and Cousin My went into the living room where the men were, leaving the door slightly open. I think the men must have been listening in to our conversation because their topic of conversation appeared to be Valentine's Day too.

"Love! It cause more argument than anything else. There should be a law banning it," Ferdie my Cousin Babsie's husband was saying.

"Don't be such an old grouch, Uncle Ferdie," Lolly said. "It's been around for centuries and I think it's here to stay so get used to it."

"Tomek's taking me out for a romantic meal for Valentine's day," Cousin Myra said. "He's picking me up in a limousine."

"A money him have fi waste," my Uncle Al said kissing his teeth.

"Are you saying I'm not worth spending money on, Al?" Cousin My asked standing threateningly in front of him with her hands on her hips.

"Er... no... no man of course mi not saying that. You deserve a nice night out. I'm just saying people spend too much money just for one day and it noh prove nothing."

"Ahoh!" Cousin My said sitting down. "I know he's getting the limo at a discount price anyway because he works for the company."

"Yu wan' try waste some money like that on me occasionally," Aunty Bliss, Uncle Al's wife shouted to him.

"Al didn't mean anything My. That's really nice but what did you tell my Babsie for? Now she wants to know why mi caan do the same," Ferdie said.

"I don't know how dem dead man ya who noh did know nut'n 'bout woman when dem alive can cause soh much trouble fi us guys yu know," Uncle Al complained.

"Mmm," Ferdie agreed. "If St Valentine was a priest dem wasn't allow to get married in dem days deh? What him would know about what woman want anyway?"

"Exactly! Dem lock up ina... ina... priestery or monastery all dem life a pray and read dem bible an' write bout t'ings dem noh know nut'n 'bout!" Uncle Al said.

"There's no such thing as a priestery, Uncle Al," Lolly said.

"All di Casanova him... A run up and down baddah woman all over di place. Babsie always a talk 'bout how men not romantic like that anymore. Because wi a real man, that's why."

"Well mi t'ink he was just a show off and a liar," Uncle Al said. "All dem woman deh would an ruin any man structure."

"You two don't have a romantic bone in your body," Cousin My said to Uncle Al and Ferdie. She got up and walked out of the room in disgust.

"At least wi not just bones!" Uncle Al shouted. "Wi still alive and Valentine and Casanova dead! Hee hee hee!"

"That's true soh we have one over on dem already," Ferdie added laughing. "I don't need to be romantic. Babsie should know seh mi love har 'cos all year mi do di job dem weh she noh like doing."

"Like what?" Uncle Al asked.

"Mi clean di oven, mi wash har car an' put air ina di tyre dem, mi let har warm har cold feet on mi at night so why because of one stupid day mi have fi buy flowers fi £30 weh cost £5 from ASDA di week before and chocolates weh she a goh give weh because she noh want put on weight."

"Aaaay... see it deh!" Uncle Al cried. "Bliss get upset if mi noh buy har chocolate but she get even more upset if mi buy dem cause she seh mi deliberately trying to make her get fat."

"Yu just caan win wid dem woman ya yu know," Ferdie said. "dem confuse yu brain man."

"Mi all cut Bliss toenail dem fi har 'cos she caan reach har foot dem noh more an' rub har bad back wid ointment. Yu not doing that fi somebody yu noh love. What yu seh 'bout dat, Mixer?" In the next room listening keenly, I perked up my ears to hear what Michael, who had been quietly watching TV so far, had to say on the subject. He cleared his throat.

"Well mi sorry yu know guys but mi caan agree wid yu on dat one," Michael, better known as Mixer, answered to my surprise.

"What yu mean?" Ferdie asked.

"Well... mi kinda have this one covered this year yu know guys. Kelly always do something nice for me on Valentine's Day so this year, I'm going to cook dinner for her, yu know romantic candlelight, wine, run her a nice perfumed bath when she gets home from work." You could have heard a pin drop. Although I couldn't see Uncle Al and Ferdie I could just imagine them looking at him opened mouthed. To be fair, Michael can be romantic when he wants to be. The problem is he doesn't want to be very often. It had taken years of careful nurturing and much shouting to get him to where I wanted.

"Way to go, Dad!" Lolly shouted.

"Keep quiet, Lolly," Uncle Al said kissing his teeth again. "Yu a likkle girl and this is man business. Why yu not in di kitchen wid di woman dem?"

"She's watching TV Al man; leave her alone," Michael said.

"Glad to see you're making an effort this year, Dad, because you know you don't like sleeping by yourself in the spare room."

I heard Michael clear his throat as Uncle Al and Ferdie just cracked up, laughing.

"Laura, didn't you just hear yu Uncle Al said to be quiet," he said.

"So Kelly put yu ina di spare room Mixer because yu forget Valentine's Day? An' yu a gwaan like yu a Mr goodie goodie?"

"Okay, soh mi forget last year. No problem. That's why I'm making up for it this year."

"All right but keep yu voice down man!" Ferdie hissed. "It's bad enough already. If my Babsie hear yu she wi want bath and candlelit dinner to an yu know seh mi caan cook. Mi figet di card to last year but mi did buy har a oxtail dinner from Chicken Run, wid extra dumpling."

"Yu a show us up, Mixer man," Uncle Al said. "A jus' show off yu a show off to yu know."

"No, seriously guys," Michael said. "Yu need to get with it," he lowered his voice and we had to creep nearer to the door to listen, "Yu have to get in touch with your feelings... you know your feminine side."

"What!" Ferdie cried. "What feminine side? Yu crazy? Mi look like mi gay to yu?"

"No that's not what I mean. I mean the modern man has to learn to be more sensitive to keep the modern woman happy." Babsie turned and looked at me with raised eyebrows.

"Did you know Michael had a feminine side?" she whispered. All I could do was shrug. If he had he'd kept it well hidden over the years.

"Mixer, I think you spending too much time in London," Ferdie said. "Northern men don't have a feminine side; definitely not northern black men anyway."

"I promise you guys, the rewards of discovering your sensitive side are well worth it, if yu know what I mean?" Michael said with a chuckle. "Lolly, go and see if yu mother need any help in the kitchen?" They obviously didn't know that we were in the next room listening and trying hard not to laugh and give ourselves away.

"Yeah...?" Uncle Al asked. "Come Ferdie man, listen up. Maybe is time wi get modernise fi true. Wi might learn some new tricks from di yoot 'ere." As Lolly opened the door, we saw them lean closer to Michael, heads together like a group of conspirators

"Soh Mixer, tell mi somet'ing...what yu cooking and what kind a perfume yu put ina di bath den?" Uncle Al asked.

"Well... first you have to..." Michael said but the rest was cut off as he closed the door.

Conspirators' plots usually cause harm to someone but these conspirators were planning to spread love so we left them to it and went back to finish cooking their dinner. I knew I could trust Michael not to let Uncle Al and Ferdie do anything that would end in tears.

We were not privy to any more of the men's plans but on Valentine's Day, Cousin My was duly picked up by Tomek her Polish 'gentleman' in a stretch limo, complete with champagne and taken out to dinner at an expensive restaurant in town. She pressed one of the roses she received and now uses it as a book mark in her bible. Cousin Babsie, Aunty Bliss and I had dinner cooked for us which we were served after having a luxury bubble bath, lovingly set by our respective partners. Cousin Babsie and Aunty Bliss were gracious enough not to let it slip that they knew Michael had done all the cooking and coached the other two men in the art of romantic table setting complete with candles and flowers in a vase. I can't speak for Ferdie and Uncle Al, and to be honest I'd rather not go there, but I know Michael was suitably rewarded for his efforts and is planning to repeat our Valentine's evening often for no particular reason at all except to spread a little love.

On my way home from work on Valentine's Day, Lolly and I popped in to visit my mother. When Mum opened the door, she looked ten years younger with a beaming smile on her face. She had done her hair and was wearing lipstick.

"You look nice. Are you going somewhere special?" I asked.

"No, I just come back from taking some flowers to the cemetery. I had to go and tell your father not to be jealous." Lolly and I looked at her, puzzled.

"As it's such a nice day," she continued, "I walked back to get some fresh air." Mum's eyes followed mine as I noticed the large Valentine's card with red heart and ribbon next to a vase of flowers on the coffee table.

"Oh... who are those from?" I asked.

"Hee hee hee!" she laughed like a girl. "Mi noh know. Imagine mi get Valentine card and flowers at my age. I was feeling a bit down this morning but it really made my day when the delivery man brought them." As I picked up the card, I happened to glance at Lolly's face and the penny dropped. With a very suspicious smile she put her finger to her lips and shook her head. The familiar handwriting read:

"To Miss Mala, the sweetest lady in Manchester. From your secret admirer."

The card smelled strongly of aftershave. It was a familiar scent because it was Michael's favourite and was sitting on our bathroom shelf at home.

"Oh Grandma, you little devil. Have you got a boyfriend?" Lolly said, winking at me as she planted a noisy kiss on her grandmother's cheek. "See, you're always saying you're getting old but you still have pulling power." I had to smile as I saw how happy that thoughtful gesture from my daughter had made her grandmother. Regardless of who had sent it, the card had put a spring in her step and a broad smile on her face.

St Valentine, whatever his origin, might have been long dead and gone but he was still spreading love and putting smiles on people's faces. And in today's world, that can't be a bad thing.

MICKY

Funny thing autism; when I say funny, obviously I don't mean amusing. No-one who experiences autism first hand would think it is amusing, but fascinating it certainly is.

Take my brother, Micky, for example. John Michael, to give him his full name, was named after my father, John Paul. Both of my brothers are named after him. My other brother is John Joseph. My father was in turn named after his father, John Adolphus. It is important for me to clarify my brother's identity because he can't do it for himself.

Micky was diagnosed with autism at the age of three. All the family knew long before then that 'something' was not as it should be. None of us knew what that 'something' was and my mother was in denial so we went along with the pretence for her sake. After Micky's diagnosis, none of the specialists could say exactly what was wrong with him or how it had happened or even give an accurate prognosis for his future. We were just told that he was somewhere on the mysterious 'autistic spectrum' that incorporates a myriad of degrees of inability to relate socially to other people and the world.

It has been exhausting and frustrating most of the time, extremely difficult sometimes not to mention heart breaking for my parents to cope with Micky because he lives on the edge of two worlds and does not conform easily to the usual boundaries. He has made us all laugh and he has made us cry. He finds it difficult to make any sense of the real world and we on the outside find it difficult to make sense of his shadow world which propels him to act and react in ways which are different to that which is accepted as 'the norm'.

Most people don't realise that people who suffer from autism are unique in their own way according to where they fall on the so called 'autistic spectrum'. We have been privileged occasionally to get a glimpse behind the mysterious curtain and see that incredible spark but I don't think any of my family fully appreciate the opportunity we have been given to experience innocence in its purest form.

Many autistic people appear to have an unfathomable ability to think 'outside the box' – an ability we have as children but lose as we become adults. I've met or been made aware of people who suffer from autism who are brilliant artists or mathematicians. Some seem to have an almost 'ESP'-like quality – an ability, although a part of the brain seems to be shrouded behind that curtain, which gives them perceptions which leaves lesser mortals stunned.

From the age of about one, although it was thought there was something wrong with his hearing, Micky could hum nursery rhymes and tunes on the radio, perfectly from beginning to end. When he began to speak at about four years old, although he never spoke directly to anyone for several years, he sang songs and repeated nursery rhymes and random facts after hearing them only once.

If you ask him to write anything apart from his first name, Micky struggles, yet, when he is ready, he will take his note pad, which he always has to hand, and a pen and write out the names of TV programmes or films and the names of characters, spelling difficult words perfectly. Although he is unable to tell the time, he knows exactly when his favourite TV programmes are due to start and what channel they are on.

At age twelve, Micky could tell you the names of the kings and queens of England and the dates they reigned from Henry V111 to Elizabeth 11. He never remembered any king prior to Henry no matter how many times he was told.

Micky also appeared to have the power of prediction. I remember him predicting Margaret Thatcher winning the 1979 elections by reciting all the prime ministers from Winston Churchill and ended with Margaret Thatcher, months before she was elected.

Last year, my Uncle Al and his best friend Ferdie, along with my brother John Joseph, otherwise known as JJ, all met up at my mother's house to watch the Brazilian Grand Prix with Micky. They often did that when a big football, cricket match or other important sporting event was taking place to make Micky feel included. I decided to go round and help Mum to cook dinner for them all and just happened to arrive at the crucial moment when the house erupted into mayhem. They had all put a bet on because Micky had predicted that Lewis Hamilton would win.

"Hamilton takes the crown," he said again and again for days before the race.

As I opened the living room door, JJ had his head in his hands and was groaning.

"What! Ah Man!" he shouted, jumping up out of his chair.

Sebastian Vettel had just spectacularly overtaken Lewis Hamilton. Hamilton was struggling to pass Timo Glock. I know a bit about motor racing because my partner Michael and daughter Laura (Lolly) are also avid fans and were only absent from the gathering because they were working. Uncle Al had put a hefty bet on Hamilton winning and was perched anxiously on the edge of the sofa with his arms folded on top of his head.

"Come on lad! You've got to pass Glock!" he shouted.

"Hamilton takes the crown," Micky said over his shoulder to no-one in particular.

"No mate," JJ said, shaking his head. "Not this time. It's over; there's no way he's going to pass Glock in time. He has to get fifth place to win, Micky, remember?"

"Hamilton takes the crown," Micky said again. He wasn't even looking at the TV but somewhere into the air as he usually did.

"No, Micky," JJ said patiently. "He's lost it, mate. Want a cup of tea?"

"Want a cup of tea?" Micky repeated as if asking himself before answering, "Yes please JJ, Micky wants a cup of tea, please." He usually spoke about himself in the third person. "Micky wants a cup of tea with milk and three sugars?" he added again as if he was asking himself.

"Yes I know, mate," JJ said. "You always have a cup of tea with milk and three sugars."

"Bring me a beer JJ," Uncle Al said despondently. They had stocked Mum's fridge up earlier to celebrate their win, so confident had they been in Micky's prediction.

JJ had just walked out of the room to put the kettle on, when Uncle Al and Ferdie's screams as they leapt into the air, brought him running back. Their shouts brought my mum and sister Clara running from the kitchen. JJ threw his arms around Micky, jumping up and down as he shouted at the top of his voice. Uncle Al and Ferdie did an impromptu dance together around the room that looked a bit like a tribal quick step. Lewis Hamilton had amazingly passed Timo Glock in the last moments of the race. I don't really have that much of an interest in motor racing but, as I usually did at home with Michael and Lolly, I couldn't help being caught up in their excitement, especially as Uncle Al grabbed me and planted a noisy kiss on my cheek.

Micky sat impassively on the sofa, face expressionless but that was nothing unusual to us.

"He's won! He's won Micky! I don't believe it!" JJ shouted.

"What on earth is going on?" Mum asked. "Have you lot gone completely mad?"

"Brazilian Grand Prix, Our Mam," Micky answered, flatly. Don't ask me why but since Micky learnt to speak he has referred to mum as 'Our Mam.'

"Youngest World Champion in Formula One history, Our Mam," he added. "First black man to win."

Calmer now, Uncle Al turned to look at Micky curiously.

"Bwoy, I'd like to know is how yu know soh much when yu don' even know di days of di week?" he laughed. "Never mind eh Micky? New computer game for you, my son. You've won me a tidy sum today."

"Hamilton was being too cautious at the start," Ferdie said. "That rain nearly did for him."

"Yeah, it was because he had to stop to change to wet tyres," JJ added.

"Bet Glock wish he'd changed his tyres going up that hill."

"Bad luck Massa, old son," Uncle Al said. "You thought you had that one in the bag didn't you?"

"Massa bites the dust," Micky said to the air.

"Oh poor man; he looks so upset," Mum said. "So how comes he hasn't won if he won the race?"

"It's about points, Mum. I'll explain it to you later," JJ answered.

"Wow, that Nicole Scherzinger is a stunner," Ferdie commented as Lewis Hamilton was surrounded by his girlfriend, father, brother and the rest of the excited McLaren team.

"Don't like her," Micky said to the air. "Our Mam is prettier."

"Oh bless him," Mum said taking a sly look in the mirror and giving her hair a pat.

"Ferdie, bwoy, wi rich! Well at least him rich 'til him wife find out, eh Micky? Hee hee hee!" Uncle Al aimed a mock punch at Micky then threw his arm around his neck and gave his head a knuckle rub. The side of Micky's mouth twitched as if he was considering a smile but he thought better of it.

"'Til Babsie find out?" Ferdie asked. "Then wha' 'bout yu? Yu t'ink your Bliss gwine let yu spend a penny of dat money?"

Uncle Al's face fell as he thought about it. "A tell yu what," he whispered to Ferdie, "you don't tell Babsie nut'n an' I won't tell Bliss. Wi will tell dem wi farget to put on di bet cos Bliss di dun tell mi already fi keep weh from di betting shop since last time when mi did...er... lose di money fi di gas bill."

Uncle Al looked over his shoulder at my mum. "Yu hear Mala? Noh baddah goh seh nut'n." Mum kissed her teeth and walked back through the door.

"Mi! A idle unnuh idle. If unnuh t'ink seh mi getting involved in unnuh foolishness unnuh mek a sad mistake," she said. My sister, Clara followed her with an almost identical, don't even start that nonsense with me, look on her face.

Uncle Al turned and looked at me.

"It's nothing to do with me," I said, "But you both know what will happen don't you?"

Micky didn't have to predict this one. Of course, it ended in big trouble for both of them when my cousin Babsie and Aunty Bliss found out, with Babsie threatening divorce for the second time in a year. We could all see it coming but Uncle Al and Ferdie never learn.

Micky has predicted that Prince Harry will be the next king of England and not Charles or William. No matter how many times we explain it to him, he reels off the kings and queens of England - "Henry V111, Edward V1, Jane, Mary 1 ... ... Edward V111, George V1, Elizabeth 11, Good King Harry."

Micky rarely laughs or smiles except for the odd episode when he will just laugh uncontrollably at nothing that the rest of us can see. Occasionally when he laughs, we do know what he is laughing at but we struggle to see the joke until we go away and give it some thought.

My brother suffers from obsessive compulsive disorder or OCD. He doesn't bother too much about the rest of the house but everything in his bedroom has to be in exactly the right place and lined up with other objects or he gets confused and upset. He has always had his routine – set in stone. We have learnt over the years not to alter it unless it's absolutely necessary because it leads to problems for Micky. Changes have to be introduced slowly and carefully. Even when he appears to have taken something in his stride it's best to keep an eye on him because he will misinterpret situations, worry, about the most bizarre things and become upset and unsettled to the point where he will run away.

Micky has always been terrified of cats and young babies. Mum has a theory that it's something to do with the sounds they make. I think she could be right. Have you noticed that a cat's mewing sometimes is very similar to the cry of a young baby? He doesn't seem to mind dogs as long as they don't get too close but there is something about cats and babies that put the fear of God into him, and I mean real terror. His fear of babies seems to dissipate once they reach about six months and are more interactive. So, you can imagine my concern many years ago when I found out I was pregnant with my eldest daughter, Shari. I wondered how Micky would cope with being in close proximity to a very young baby.

I tried to prepare him by showing him photographs of babies but he became so distressed that I had to abandon that idea. As my stomach grew bigger, I explained about the baby growing in my tummy but it all seemed to go straight over Micky's head.

"Fat," he said, flatly.

For the first few weeks after Shari was born I avoided going to Mum's when Micky was there. The first time I visited with Shari and Micky was at home, he came to the door to greet me as he usually did, took one look at the carry cot as I walked in and ran to his bedroom, screaming. He refused to come out until I left. That is how it was for the first few months of Shari's life. Mum would tell Micky we had arrived as the car pulled up. He would wave at me through the window but as soon as Michael or I got the baby out of the car, Micky would make a hasty retreat to his bedroom until we left. He resisted all attempts to get him to even look at Shari, to the extent of closing his eyes tight and screaming when I took Shari to his bedroom one day.

When Shari was about four months old, Mum had a hospital appointment and asked me to go round and stay with Micky for a couple of hours. He had a cold and Mum had kept him off from the day centre where he usually went during the day. Mum reminded me that his behaviour might be unpredictable because of the change to his routine.

Micky, who had refused to take off his coat, hat and scarf since finding out that the minibus wasn't coming to pick him up, as usual bolted to his room as soon as he saw me walking up the path with Shari's carry cot.

I fed and settled Shari as I wanted to wash my hair so that my sister Clara could straighten it for me when she got home from work. I had just started to rinse my hair when Shari began to cry. I knew the sound of her crying sometimes upset Micky, so I hurriedly tried to rinse the suds away, shouting to Shari that I was coming. There was no point shouting anything to Micky as he would just ignore me. After a few moments, thankfully the crying stopped because in my haste I had managed to get shampoo into my eyes which were now stinging. I assumed that Shari had fallen asleep again so I carefully rinsed my eyes. When I had finished, I tiptoed to the top of the stairs and listened, not wanting to go downstairs in case I woke her up again. Not hearing a sound, I listened at Micky's door. I could hear his TV on but no other sound so I assumed he was okay. I put conditioner on my hair and took my time as I rinsed, listening for any more crying.

As I walked into the living room, dripping water and rubbing my hair with a towel, I gasped and stopped dead in my tracks at the sight which met me. Sitting on the sofa was Micky gazing into space with a still, limp looking Shari draped across his lap. As I was about to cry out, Micky looked around with a big grin on his face.

"Shush, Kelly... baby sleeping." Shari gave a couple of sucks on her dummy. I let out a long breath of relief and had to sit down quickly before my legs gave way. Micky knew I was in the bathroom and had heard Shari crying. He had over come his fear of babies to pick her up out of her carry cot and rock her back to sleep on his lap.

"Baby scary! Cry. Micky very brave," he said in a loud whisper.

It didn't even strike me at the time that because he had addressed me directly, I was experiencing one of Micky's rare 'open curtain' moments. I just reacted and seized my opportunity to get through to him.

"Baby isn't scary, Micky. Baby very nice," I said softly, "but yes you are very brave. Thank you. Shall I take her now?"

"No, Kel. You do hair." Micky looked down at Shari then looked up. "Baby not scary? Baby very nice?" he asked but he wasn't asking me. He was looking somewhere into the air. He had flipped back into shadow world where he usually resided. Flip. He was back again. He turned his head and looked at me. "Baby not scary; Baby like Micky, Kel."

"Yes, of course she does. She loves you."

As if to confirm that, Shari in her sleep gave a little smile and a couple more sucks on her dummy. Micky's face lit up with the biggest smile I had ever seen. His face was almost comical as he stared at Shari in absolute wonder. That was the beginning of a long, loving relationship between the two of them. From that day, my brother Micky became Shari's slave. It was amusing to watch Shari as a toddler leading the six feet tall Micky around, holding on to one of his fingers.

By the time Mum came home, Micky had not only retreated to his world but back to his room.

"Lord bless us and save us!" she cried when I told her what had happened. "John Michael is full of surprises." She went to his room where he was engrossed in one of his favourite TV programmes. As she hugged and kissed him, Micky leaned to one side, then the other, trying to see around Mum so he could continue watching his programme. When Mum came out of his room, she was wiping her eyes with a tissue. I had only ever seen my mother cry once and that was at my father's funeral.

For the first time Micky came out of his room for dinner while Shari was in the house. As I held her on my lap at the dinner table, and she squirmed and gurgled, he couldn't take his eyes off her. It was as if he was seeing her for the first time. The corner of his mouth kept twitching the way it does when he wants to smile.

"Baby not scary?" he asked the air. "Baby soft and smell nice?" Then he began to laugh for no apparent reason the way he does sometimes.

"Micky, stop that. What is so funny?" I asked.

"Our Mam soft in the head," he said.

"I'll give you soft in the head! Yu cheeky devil," Mum said. She was laughing as she piled more chicken onto is plate.

Shari's first word was "Mi". Her father got really excited because he thought she was saying 'Michael' until we went to my mum's house and Shari nearly jumped out of the car with excitement, squealing and shouting "Mi! Mi!" at the sight of Micky. Michael felt better when a few weeks later she started saying "Da Da". The only problem was for a while every black man she saw was "Da Da" which was very embarrassing on occasion.

Shari caught on very quickly that her Uncle Micky needed her protection more than she needed his. There is no doubt that she helped Micky to take a step further back from the shadow world of autism. She also helped him to overcome his fear of babies although to this day, he is still wary of very young babies and gives them a wide berth.

Shari will be thirty this year but Micky, now grey haired, still calls her "Baby". As for cats... he still hates them and freaks out every time he sees one.